AN ILLUSTRATED GUIDE TO
MODERN
DESTROYERS

pod sop
(NAV)

a Salamander book

Published by Salamander Books Limited
LONDON · NEW YORK

AN ILLUSTRATED GUIDE TO
MODERN
DESTROYERS

John Jordan

A Salamander Book

© 1986 Salamander Books Ltd.,
52 Bedford Row,
London WC1R 4LR,
United Kingdom.

ISBN 0 86101 203 8

Distributed in the United Kingdom by
Hodder & Stoughton Services,
PO Box 6, Dunton Green, Sevenoaks,
Kent TN13 2XX.

Credits

Author: John Jordan is a contributor to
many important defence journals,
co-author of Salamander's *Balance of
Military Power* and *Modern Weapons*,
and author of four companion "Guid
– *The Modern US Navy*, *The Moder
Soviet Navy*, *Modern Naval Aviatio
Battleships and Battlecruisers*.

Managing Editor: Philip
Designer: Roger Ch
Typeset: The C
Printed:
Production, Turnhout,

Contents

Introduction

I N 1939 there would have been no problem in defining the term "destroyer". That this is no longer the case in the mid-1980s is testimony to the major changes in configuration, mission and armament which have affected the type since World War II, and to the current confusion in terminology which surrounds vessels in this category. The distinction made between a "destroyer" and a "frigate" in the British Royal Navy is different from that which prevails in the US Navy, and this particular disagreement is reflected in the classification systems employed by other navies. A further anomaly in the US Navy's elevation of large numbers of unarmoured carrier escorts derived from the destroyer type to the status of "cruiser" during the 1970s.

The reader may quarrel with the selection of classes included in this volume. Yet, in a sense, the argument for or against the inclusion (or omission) of a certain class focuses on the principal theme of this introduction, which is the historical development of the modern destroyer and of the various missions which have been assigned to ships in this category over the period. The reader may not, in the end, be provided with a working definition of the term "destroyer", but it is hoped that he will know why some ships are designated destroyers by some navies, while other ships similar in size and general capabilities belonging to other navies are not.

The Postwar Period
The destroyer of the prewar era had been an uncomplicated ship with an anti-surface mission, designed to

attack enemy battleships with torpedoes and to fend off similar attacks made on friendly capital ships by employing its quick-firing medium-calibre guns. Only a handful of machine guns were carried for self-protection against air attack.

By the end of World War II, however, the principal destroyer mission had become that of fleet air defence. Radar-controlled dual-purpose mountings were steadily replacing the low-angle anti-surface weapons, and destroyers were being fitted with increasing numbers of light anti-aircraft guns of 40mm and 20mm calibre. Some US Navy destroyers were fitted out as radar pickets, and carried large air surveillance and height-finding radars. Anti-submarine warfare was also becoming more important, and advanced sonars, together with new types of rocket launchers and mortars, were under development for the US Navy and the Royal Navy. Fears regarding the future size and quality of the Soviet submarine fleet served only to accelerate these developments.

In order to accommodate all these new weapons systems, destroyers became larger and heavier: the average prewar destroyer had a standard displacement of about 1,600 tons; the "general-purpose" des-

Right: *Valdés,* one of five modernised units of the war-built Fletcher class to be transferred from the US Navy to Spain. One quintuple bank of torpedo tubes has been landed, and there are three twin 3in AA guns and modern radars.

Above: The Australian destroyer *Vampire* in the late 1970s. The large 4.5in Mk 6 gun mountings are testimony to the weight penalties incurred by postwar destroyers in the pursuit of effective air defence.

troyers of the US Navy's Forrest Sherman class built during the early/mid-1950s displaced 2,750 tons; while the larger carrier escorts of the Mitscher class came out at 3,700 tons. There was increasing concern about the number of ships which could be af-forded should this process continue, and it was already becoming increasingly clear that the pressures on destroyer displacement would eventually lead to hard choices being made between the weapons systems available. ▶

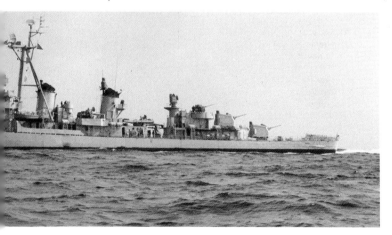

▶ To a certain extent, mission specialisation was already present. The destroyers designed in the late 1940s and early 1950s were built primarily for the fleet air defence role. It was initially thought that carrier task forces would be relatively invulnerable to submarine attack because of their high speed, and a clear distinction was therefore made in all Western navies between air defence ships designed to accompany carriers (destroyers), and antisubmarine vessels designed to escort mercantile convoys (destroyer escorts/frigates). Convoy escorts were generally smaller and slower than destroyers: single-shaft propulsion and diesels were frequently adopted to give the ships the necessary endurance, and a maximum speed of 25–27kt was generally accepted. However, the British, who were impressed by the improvement in underwater performance revealed by captured German Type XXI submarines and were also concerned about possible developments in closed-cycle propulsion, built "quality" frigates with first-rate propulsion systems capable of driving them at around 30kt. This was to have important consequences for the subsequent development of the destroyer in the Royal Navy.

The Missile Revolution

The pressures on destroyer size were further increased by the advent of the guided missile. The missiles themselves weighed relatively little, but their magazines and handling rooms took up a considerable part of the ship's hull volume. Moreover, surface-to-air missiles required large numbers of radar antennae mounted high in the ship, bringing considerable problems of topweight. Extensive use had to be made of aluminium alloy for superstructures, at the cost of lower resistance to blast and fire damage.

The advent of the nuclear-powered submarine posed additional problems. Carrier escorts could no longer afford to concentrate on air defence, as the broad areas over which carrier task

Development of Air Defence Destroyers 1955–85

	Surcouf (Fr.)	Charles F. Adams (USA)	Sheffield (UK)
Completed	1955–57	1960–64	1975–83
Displacement	2,750 tons	3,370 tons	3,150 tons
Air defence weapons	3 twin 5in (127mm) DP 3 twin 57mm AA 4 single 20mm AA	1 single/twin-arm launcher for Tartar missiles 2 single 5in (127mm) DP	1 twin-arm launcher for Sea Dart missiles 2 single 20mm AA
Anti-submarine weapons	2 triple 21.7in (550mm) TT	1 8-cell launcher for ASROC missiles; 2 triple 12.75in (324mm) TT	1 WG.13 Lynx helicopter 2 triple 12.75in (324mm) TT
Anti-surface weapons	(Main guns) 2 triple 21.7in (550mm) TT	(Main guns)	1 4.5in (114mm) DP (Sea Dart missiles)
Propulsion/speed	Steam turbines/ 34kt	Steam turbines/ 35kt	Gas turbines (COGOG)/30kt

Below: *Robinson* (DDG-12), one of 23 general-purpose destroyers built for the US Navy during the early 1960s. She has missiles both for air defence and for anti-submarine work.

forces would be spread to minimise the effects of nuclear attack demanded that the escorts cope with fast-manoeuvring submarines which had broken through the outer ring of defences. Advanced sonars, anti-submarine missiles and facilities for manned and unmanned helicopters would be required in addition to area defence missile systems. The US Navy took the logical step of creating a new category, the "frigate" (DLG), which was derived from the large destroyer leaders (DL) built in the early 1950s. The size of these large carrier escorts was such that many of them were classified as cruisers (CG) in the mid-1970s. The French Navy built two similar ships (Suffren class), also designated "frigates" (*frégates*), to escort the new carriers of the Clemenceau class, and Britain designed similar escorts for a projected new generation of carriers. However the British, for whom the term "frigate" referred to an anti-submarine convoy escort, persisted with the "destroyer" classification for the Type 82 class.

Following the completion of the general-purpose missile destroyers of the Charles F. Adams class in the mid-1960s, US Navy destroyers would be built either for the anti-submarine mission (the Spruance class) or for the air defence mission (the Arleigh Burke class). A specialised mission was also a feature of most French destroyers of the period. In the early 1960s four of the conventional gun-armed air defence escorts of the Surcouf class ▶

Development of Anti-Submarine Destroyers 1955-85

	Friesland (Neth.)	*Takatsuki* (Jap.)	*Georges Leygues* (Fr.)
Completed	1956–58	1967–70	1979 onwards
Displacement	2,500 tons	3,200 tons	3,830 tons
Anti-submarine weapons	2 4-barrelled Bofors rocket launchers	3 DASH ASW drones 1 8-cell launcher for ASROC missiles 1 4-barrelled Bofors rocket launcher 2 triple 12.75in (324mm) TT	2 WG.13 Lynx helicopters 2 catapults for 10 L5 torpedoes
Air defence weapons	2 twin 4.7in (120mm) DP 6 single 40mm AA	2 single 5in (127mm) DP	1 8-cell launcher for Crotale missiles 1 3.9in (100mm) DP 2 single 20mm AA
Anti-surface weapons	(Main guns)	(Main guns)	4 MM38 Exocet missiles (Main gun)
Propulsion/speed	Steam turbines/ 36kt	Steam turbines/ 32kt	Gas turbines plus diesels for cruising (CODOG)/ 30kt

▶ were taken in hand for conversion to air defence vessels, and five other units of the class subsequently underwent an ASW conversion. When the French came to consider replacements for these ships, they opted for air defence and anti-submarine variants of the same C70 design.

Below: The French *Dupleix* typifies the trend towards a specialised mission for ships of destroyer size. She is optimised for ASW operations, and has only limited air defence capabilities.

Above: Destroyers of the Soviet and Chinese Navies (the photo is of a Chinese Luda class ship) were initially intended to protect national waters against incursions by Western carrier task forces.

The British, on the other hand, already had first-line vessels capable of fleet speed for the anti-submarine mission. The series of "quality" frigates derived from the postwar Type 12 design were no longer seen exclusively as convoy escorts but were increasingly employed as fleet units,

leaving ships in the "destroyer" category to specialise in fleet air defence. The design which has recently superseded the Type 12, the Type 22 (Broadsword) class, is significantly larger than the Type 42 air defence destroyers of the Birmingham/Manchester class and approximates more closely in size and capabilities to the US Navy's Spruance, but it is classified by the Royal Navy as a "frigate" (and is therefore not featured in this volume).

Soviet Perspectives
In the immediate postwar period the Soviet Navy built conventional destroyers armed with dual-purpose guns and anti-ship torpedoes which were classified as *eskadrenny minonosets* (EM, literally "fleet minelaying ships" – an interesting insight into traditional Soviet destroyer missions). With the advent of guided missiles, however, new categories were established which classified ships in terms of their size and mission. Ships below cruiser size are classified *bol'shoy korabl'* (large ships), and the words *raketny* (missile, anti-ship) or *protivolodochny* (anti-submarine) are inserted to denote mission; there is no ▶

▶ "air defence" mission, because Soviet surface ships do not operate in task forces centred on aircraft carriers. Omitted from this volume are the BPKs of the Kresta and Kara classes, which have both major air defence and anti-submarine systems and therefore correspond closely in size and capabilities to the large US Navy carrier escorts; the US Navy describes these two classes of Soviet ship as "cruisers".

Weapons Development since World War II

Destroyers built in the immediate postwar period were typically armed with two or three twin dual-purpose gun mountings of between 4.5in (114mm) and 5.1in (130mm) calibre for the air defence and anti-surface missions. Unlike the hand-loaded models of prewar design, the mountings were in general fully automatic and radar-controlled, and consequently they were larger, heavier and more complex than their prewar counterparts. The medium-calibre DP guns were backed up by heavy radar-controlled AA guns, the favoured calibres being 40mm, 57mm and 3in/76mm. The small hand-worked 20mm Oerlikon which had been widely fitted in destroyers in the late war period was gradually disappearing because of its recognised lack of effectiveness against high-speed jet aircraft.

Some postwar destroyers, notably those built for the Soviet and Swedish Navies, retained a heavy armament of torpedoes. However, in most of the destroyers completed for the Western navies, anti-ship torpedoes gave way to anti-submarine weapons, i.e. rocket launchers, mortars and ASW torpedoes.

New Air Defence Weapons

The US Navy was the first to abandon the twin dual-purpose gun mounting in favour of the high-performance single mounting. However, the standard US 5in (127mm) calibre was retained to ensure effective performance in the anti-surface role. West European navies had traditionally preferred a smaller-calibre gun for air defence, and in the late 1950s new single dual-purpose mountings of 3.9in (100mm) and 4in (102mm)

calibre emerged. Four mountings (two forward, two aft) were generally favoured, and this was the arrangement adopted for the original design of the French *La Galissonnière*, the German *Hamburg*, and the two destroyers of the Almirante Riveros class built in a British shipyard for Chile.

Meanwhile the US Navy, with the British Royal Navy and the Soviet Navy close behind, was already well advanced in the development of surface-to-air missiles which would effectively supersede the dual-purpose gun mounting in the air defence role. The early models were large and ungainly, and required complex handling arrangements comprising storage magazines, fin/booster assembly rooms and testing areas. Their guidance radars were heavy and had to be carried high in the ship, as did the long-range air surveillance and height-finding radars required to provide target data. Missiles like the US Talos and Terrier, the British Sea Slug and French Masurca required large ships to carry them, which tended to push these ships out of the traditional destroyer category. The US Navy's development of the small medium-range Tartar missile, neatly packaged in a cylindrical ready-use magazine topped by a twin-arm Mk 11 or single-arm Mk 13 launcher and paired with lightweight SPG-51 fire control radars, answered a number of prayers, and Tartar was widely adopted by other pro-Western navies. The British attempted to fulfil the same requirement with their Sea Dart missile, but although long-range performance was far better than that of Tartar, Sea Dart proved to be a heavier, more volume-intensive system, and attempts to sell the missile outside the Royal Navy (notably to the Netherlands and China) were unsuccessful.

The Soviets chose to adapt a land-based missile, the SA-3 Goa, for shipboard use. The SA-N-1 system which resulted is on the heavy side for installation in destroyers, and employs a form of radar/command guidance now regarded as outmoded. The missile employs a stabilised launcher, suggesting that there were early problems of acquisition from a rolling ship. The latest Soviet medium-range air defence system designed for destroyer installation is the SA-N-7, a

Above: The launch of a Seacat missile. Even destroyers whose primary mission is anti-submarine warfare must be fitted with close-range systems such as this for self-defence.

system similar in concept to the US Navy's Tartar/Standard, employing a single-arm launcher and semi-active guidance.

Medium-range missiles such as those described above were fitted exclusively in destroyers whose primary mission was area air defence. However, there was also a requirement for smaller short-range air defence systems to enable vessels with a primary anti-submarine mission to protect themselves against air attack. Here the British were the first to develop a viable system: Seacat was fitted in County class destroyers and improved Type 12 frigates during the early 1960s. The Americans followed up with Sea Sparrow (in service 1967), launched from a modified ASROC launcher and installed largely in frigates and carriers; this was superseded ten years later by NATO Sea Sparrow, a multi-national ▶

Below: Even modern area defence missile systems consume vast quantities of space. Beneath the compact twin-arm launcher of HMS *Gloucester* is a magazine housing 40 Sea Dart missiles.

Above: Modern Italian surface ships are fitted with the Aspide close-range air defence missile. It provides protection against hostile aircraft out to a range of approximately 8nm (15,000m).

▶ development employing a modified Sparrow missile with folding wings and more compact stowage. Sea Sparrow has been adopted by a number of pro-Western navies, but the French chose to develop their own system, Crotale, which entered service in the late 1970s. Large Soviet anti-submarine vessels completed in the 1970s were generally fitted with area defence systems to compensate for the lack of carrier air support, but the latest ASW destroyers of the Udaloy class will be fitted with a missile system with an effective range similar to that of Sea Sparrow, the SA-N-8.

The latest trends in destroyer air defence centre on vertical launch and fixed, electronically-scanned radar arrays. Fixed arrays such as the US SPY-1 provide much-enhanced coverage and tracking of air targets and quicker reaction times, and make possible multiple target engagement (earlier systems are restricted by the number of missile fire control radars fitted). Vertical launch assists multiple target engagement in that the missiles can be fired directly from the containers in which they are housed and do not have to be loaded on to a launcher. Other advantages, especially those of missile readiness and quick reaction, make vertical launch par-

ticularly attractive for short-range air defence missiles, and the Soviet SA-N-8 system employs this launch mode in preference to a trainable launcher.

Anti-submarine Warfare

Developments in anti-submarine warfare since World War II have been every bit as dramatic as those in air defence. The mortars and rocket launchers developed in the immediate postwar period had typical ranges of 1,000–2,000yd, ranges which corresponded to the maximum detection ranges of contemporary sonars. They fired their depth bombs in a set pattern in order to bracket the latest known position of the submarine. A number of navies, notably the US and the French, also showed an interest in developing precision weapons in the form of homing torpedoes. Short anti-submarine torpedoes, which had a similar effective range to the mortars and rocket launchers, proved very successful, and the US Mk 44 and Mk 46 torpedoes, fired from triple Mk 32 tubes, were widely adopted by other Western navies. Long anti-submarine torpedoes, which in the early 1950s seemed the logical way to extend the range of the ship's weapons to match the detection ranges possible with the new sonars being developed, have generally been less successful because of the difficulties inherent in providing a satisfactory form of control for the surface ship in order to counteract evasive manoeuvres by the submarine during the torpedo's run-out.

Fortunately, the advent of the guided missile provided a solution to the problem of long-range ASW engagements. In 1961 the US Navy brought into service the ASROC missile, launched from an eight-cell box. ASROC carried either a nuclear depth bomb or a Mk 44 homing torpedo out to a range of about 10,000yd (9,000m), a figure which corresponded to the maximum theoretical detection range of the SQS-23 sonar. The French Navy developed a similar torpedo-carrying missile, Malafon, shortly afterwards, followed by the Australian Navy with Ikara and eventually by the Soviet Navy with the SS-N-14 (in service 1970). These later missiles differ from ASROC in one important respect: whereas ASROC is a simple ballistic rocket, the others are cruise missiles which can be guided in flight by the mother ship. This enables them to respond to the latest data inputs from the ship's sonar. However, the missiles are all somewhat bulkier than ASROC, and therefore require large handling rooms.

A parallel solution to the problem of long-range engagement of submarine targets was the helicopter. The US Navy initially favoured an unmanned platform designated DASH (Drone Anti-Submarine Helicopter) and capable of carrying two Mk 44 torpedoes. DASH was also adopted by the Japanese Maritime Self-Defence Force, but the drone proved difficult to control from the mother ship and the system was finally abandoned by the US Navy in the late 1960s (the JMSDF continued to operate DASH into the late 1970s). At the same time, however, a number of European navies were experimenting successfully with the manned helicopter, the British Wasp and the Italian AB.204 being particularly prominent. In 1970 the Soviet Navy began to operate the Ka-25 Hormone anti-submarine helicopter from BPKs, and the US Navy finally decided in favour of the manned helicopter in 1971, when it developed the SH-2 Seasprite. One of the attractions of the Seasprite was that it was small enough to be operated from many of the ships fitted for DASH.

However, a clear distinction needs to be drawn between the small manned helicopters developed for the West European navies and those operated by the US and Soviet Navies. The early European models were simply weapons carriers, relying exclusively on sonar data from the mother ship to launch their torpedoes. The Soviet and US helicopters, on the other hand, carried underwater sensors of their own in the form of dunking sonar and/or sonobuoys and magnetic ▶

Below: The Japanese destroyers of the Hatsuyuki class deploy three major anti-submarine systems: an HSS-2B Sea King helicopter, an 8-cell launcher for ASROC missiles, and triple tubes for Mk 46 torpedoes.

anomaly detectors (MAD), and were therefore capable of making their attacks at longer range. This was considered particularly important by the US Navy, as the latest ship sonars of the SQS-26 series were capable of detection at twice the range of ASROC using the "direct path" or "bottom bounce" modes and under favourable sonar conditions could obtain a crude position on a submarine target out to the first convergence zone (30–35nm, 55–65km). The most recent European ASW helicopters, the Anglo-French Lynx and the Italian AB.212, have similar detection capabilities but are smaller than the US and Soviet models and therefore have lower endurance and a limited payload.

Perhaps the most interesting development in the history of helicopter deployment aboard destroyers was the adoption of the large Sea King, essentially a carrier-borne helicopter, by the Canadian Navy in the early 1960s. In endurance and payload the Sea King far surpasses any other shipborne helicopter currently in service, and when the JMSDF finally abandoned DASH in the late 1970s it decided to follow a similar course.

The Anti-Surface Mission

From 1945 until about the mid-1960s the anti-surface mission in Western navies was performed by attack aircraft operating from carriers. The Soviet surface fleet of the period was relatively small and insignificant, and the West was therefore slow to develop anti-ship missiles for tactical use. The Soviet Navy, on the other hand, possessed no aircraft carriers and was faced by large numbers of Western surface vessels: as a result, it was well to the fore in the development of surface-to-surface missiles, and the SS-N-1 Scrubber was in service aboard Soviet destroyers from about 1960.

When in 1967 the Israeli destroyer

Eilat was sunk by a single Soviet-built SS-N-2 Styx missile the Western position was reviewed with some urgency. The main efforts of the US Navy and the Royal Navy were at first directed into anti-missile defence but the French, whose surface warships frequently undertook independent deployments to distant stations, developed the revolutionary Exocet sea-skimming missile. The ease with which the missile could be installed made it immediately attractive to other navies, and both the British and Germans purchased Exocet for their own destroyers. The US Navy chose to develop its own missile, Harpoon, which entered service in 1977 and was widely adopted by other pro-Western navies, notably the Netherlands and Japan. Harpoon has a different flight profile from that of Exocet and has greater range. It has folding fins and is generally deployed in a particularly compact installation of two groups of four cylindrical canisters. The latest version of the French Exocet, the MM40, employs similar technology.

Soviet missiles are very large in comparison with their Western counterparts. They have an aeroplane configuration with folding wings and are generally fired from angled ramps inside a cylindrical launcher. They therefore make greater space

Right: The Soviet Navy has placed more stress on the anti-surface mission during the postwar era than have Western navies. Here a destroyer of the Kashin-Mod class shadows the British anti-submarine carrier *Illustrious*, 19,800 tons, autumn 1985.

Above: The launch of an MM40 Exocet missile. Folding fins, which deploy automatically as the missile leaves its container, make for a particularly compact installation. Missiles such as these have had a major impact on surface warfare over recent years.

demands on the ship which carries them. On the other hand they carry a much heavier warhead than Western SSMs, a feature which probably derives from the original Soviet anti-carrier mission. The latest SS-N-22 missile, carried by the destroyers of the Sovremenny class, has a range similar to that of Harpoon.

The long range of modern anti-ship missiles brings with it the problem of over-the-horizon targeting. Some Soviet destroyers carry a specially-adapted variant of the Ka-25 helicopter (the Hormone-B) for missile targeting. The US Navy's Seasprite helicopter has a similar secondary role, and the latest West European helicopters, unlike earlier models, are fitted with a surface search radar. The Anglo-French Lynx has its own missile capability; it can launch AS-12 or Sea Skua anti-ship missiles against small warships.

Almirante Brown class

Completed: 1983–84.
Names: D 3 *Almirante Brown*; D 4 *La Argentina*; D 5 *Heroina*; D 6 *Sarandí*.
Displacement: 2,900 tons standard; 3,360 tons full load.
Dimensions: Length 413ft (125.9m) oa; beam 49ft (15m); draught 19ft (5.8m) max.
Propulsion: 2-shaft COGOG; 2 Olympus TM3B gas turbines, 51,600hp = 30.5kt; 2 Tyne RM1C gas turbines, 10,200hp.
Weapons: *AAW*: 1 8-cell Albatros launcher (24 Aspide missiles); 8 40mm (4 × 2) Breda-Bofors AA.
ASuW: 2 quadruple launchers for MM40 Exocet missiles; 1 5in (127mm) OTO Melara DP.
ASW: 2 WG.13 Lynx helicopters; 2 triple ILAS-3 tubes for Mk 46 torpedoes.
Sensors: *Surveillance*: DA-08A, ZW-06.
Fire control: WM-25, STIR, LIROD GFCS 4 (2).
Sonars: Atlas 80.
Complement: 200.

These ships belong to the MEKO 360 series pioneered as a private venture by the West German Blohm & Voss shipyard. They were ordered in 1978 as a class of six, with the proviso that four would be built in Argentina with German assistance, but in 1979, when the MEKO 140-type corvettes were ordered, the order was modified to four, with construction exclusively by Blohm & Voss.

The MEKO principle involves the design of a range of standard hulls into which modular weapons and electronics units selected by the customer from an international range of equipment can be fitted. The modules are of fixed dimensions, with standard interconnections to provide electrical power, compressed air, cooling water and data/control links. The principal advantage of the system is that the hulls can be built in a very short period of time, and the weapons systems can be tested independently prior to installation. Maintenance and replacement of the weapons systems and electronics can be performed with comparative ease. The only significant disadvantage is that the large openings in the decks require additional strengthening of the hull structure, with consequent weight penalties.

The weapons, with the exception of the French MM40 Exocet missiles, are of Italian design and manufacture, while the electronics are Dutch. The Albatros launcher has a 16-missile reload magazine located in the deckhouse on which the DA-08 air surveillance radar and the STIR tracker radar are mounted. The WM-25 radar atop the foremast tower can control both the 127mm DP gun and the Aspide surface-to-air missiles; the twin 40mm Breda-Bofors mountings are controlled by two HSA LIROD FC radars.

Following the Anglo-Argentine confrontation over the Falkland Islands orders for four Lynx helicopters intended for this class were cancelled by the UK.

Below: *Almirante Brown* on her sea trials, still carrying her original pennant number. These four ships, built in West German shipyards, were designed on the MEKO principle, which involves the fitting of modular weapons systems in a standard hull. The 127mm and 40mm guns are of Italian origin, while the air surveillance and fire control radars were designed and manufactured in the Netherlands.

Hércules class

Completed: 1976–81.
Names: D 1 *Hércules*; D 2 *Santísima Trinidad*.
Displacement: 3,150 tons standard; 4,350 tons full load.
Dimensions: Length 410ft (125m) oa; beam 47ft (14.3m); draught 19ft (5.8m) max.
Propulsion: 2-shaft COGOG; 2 Olympus TM3B gas turbines, 54,400hp = 30kt; 2 Tyne RM1A gas turbines, 8,200hp = 18kt.
Weapons: *AAW*: 1 twin launcher for Sea Dart (20 missiles); 2 20mm (2 × 1) AA.
ASuW: 4 MM38 Exocet missiles; 1 4.5in (114mm) Mk 8 DP.
ASW: 1 WG.13 Lynx helicopter; 2 triple Mk 32 tubes for Mk 46 torpedoes.
Sensors: *Surveillance*: Type 965M, Type 992Q.
Fire control: Type 909 (2).
Sonars: Type 184M, Type 162M.
Complement: 270.

These two Type 42 destroyers were ordered from Britain in May 1970, only four months after *Sheffield*, the lead ship of the class, had been laid down. *Hércules* was built by Vickers, Barrow, but the second ship, *Santísima Trinidad*, was built at the Astilleros Navales, Río Santiago, with British assistance. In 1975, shortly after her launch, the latter ship was severely damaged by a terrorist bomb, and her completion was considerably delayed. Her work-up at Portsmouth, UK, was completed only a few months before the Argentine invasion of the Falkland Islands.

The two ships are essentially similar to the ill-fated *Sheffield*, and have the distinctive ''ears'' on the funnel which were a feature of the latter ship. They were, however, fitted from the outset with triple tubes for the Mk 46 anti-submarine torpedo, and could also be distinguished from their British counterparts by the configuration of the upper part of the mainmast.

Below: *Santísima Trinidad* was built in Argentina with British assistance. Her completion was delayed by sabotage: she was severely damaged by a terrorist bomb while fitting out.

Above: An aerial view of *Santísima Trinidad* shortly after completion. In 1982 both she and *Hércules* had four single launchers for MM38 Exocet anti-ship missiles fitted abreast the funnel.

In 1980 *Hércules* had four single launchers for MM38 Exocet missiles fitted atop the hangar. In early 1982 the launchers were relocated on platforms abreast the funnel port and starboard, the ship's boats being removed. *Santísima Trinidad* was also fitted with Exocet at this time, and both ships received ECM equipment.

During the conflict in the South Atlantic *Hércules* and her sister were employed as air defence escorts for Argentina's only aircraft carrier, *25 de Mayo*; had they joined action with the British Task Force, they would undoubtedly have come up against vessels of the same class serving with the Royal Navy. In the post-Falklands period the Argentine Navy became increasingly concerned about the problem of maintaining these vessels without the co-operation of British defence manufacturers, and there have been reports that Argentina has tried, unsuccessfully, to sell the ships to Iran.

Perth class

Completed:	1965–67.
Names:	D 38 *Perth*; D 39 *Hobart*; D 41 *Brisbane*.
Displacement:	3,370 tons standard; 4,618 tons full load.
Dimensions:	Length 440ft (134.2m) oa; beam 47ft (14.3m); draught 19ft 9in (6m) max.
Propulsion:	2-shaft geared steam turbines; 70,000shp = 33kt.
Weapons:	*AAW*: 1 single launcher Mk 13 for Standard SM-1A MR (40 missiles).
	ASW: 2 single launchers for Ikara missiles; 2 triple Mk 32 tubes for Mk 44/46 torpedoes.
	ASuW: Harpoon missiles from Mk 13 launcher; 2 5in (127mm, 2 × 1) Mk 42 DP.
Sensors:	*Surveillance*: SPS-52B, SPS-40, SPS-10.
	Fire control: SPG-51C (2), SPG-53A, Ikara control.
	Sonars: SQS-23F.
Complement:	333.

The design of these three vessels is based on the US Navy's Charles F. Adams class, but with a number of modifications specified by the Australian Navy. The first two ships, *Perth* and *Hobart,* were ordered from the United States in January 1962 and the third ship, *Brisbane,* in January 1963.

As all three ships were completed some time after the US Navy's own pro-gramme had terminated they incorporated all the improvements introduced in the later units of the Charles F. Adams class – the Mk 13 single-arm launcher, SPS-52B 3-D and SPS-40 air surveillance radars, and the SQS-23F bow sonar. In addition, the design was recast to incorporate the Australian Ikara anti-submarine missile system in place of the US ASROC launcher amidships. A large deckhouse between the funnels houses the magazine, and there are single laun-chers for Ikara port and starboard. A radome housing the guidance radar is located atop the bridge.

Below: *Hobart,* the second ship of the class. All three of the Australian ships have the SPS-40 air search and SPS-52 3-D radars, a feature of the later US Navy ships of the class.

Above: The destroyer *Brisbane* at speed. The radome housing the guidance radar for the Ikara anti-submarine missile is particularly prominent atop the bridge. The port-side launcher and the magazine deckhouse can be seen forward of the second funnel.

In 1974–75 *Perth* was modernised in the United States, when the Tartar missile was replaced by the Standard SM-1 MR, a Naval Tactical Data System (NTDS) was installed, and the Mk 42 gun mountings were modified to Mod. 10 standard. The other two ships were similarly refitted in Australia, the updates being completed in 1979. Further modifications planned, commencing in 1985, include conversion of the Mk 13 launcher and magazine to enable the ships to fire the Harpoon anti-ship missile, and the fitting of two Vulcan/Phalanx 20mm CIWS guns for anti-missile defence.

Below: *Perth* was updated in an American shipyard in 1974–75. She now fires the Standard missile in place of Tartar. Her two sisters were modernised in Australian shipyards.

CANADA

Iroquois class

Completed:	1972–73.
Names:	280 *Iroquois*; 281 *Huron*; 282 *Athabaskan*; 283 *Algonquin*.
Displacement:	3,551 tons standard; 4,200 tons full load.
Dimensions:	Length 423ft (129m) oa; beam 50ft (15.2m); draught 14ft 6in (4.4m).
Propulsion:	2-shaft COGOG; 2 FT 4A2 Pratt & Whitney gas turbines, 50,000hp = 29kt; 2 FT 12H gas turbines, 7,400hp.
Weapons:	*AAW*: 2 quadruple launchers for Sea Sparrow (32 missiles). *ASW*: 2 Sea King CH-124 helicopters; 2 triple Mk 32 tubes for Mk 44/46 torpedoes; 1 Mk 10 Limbo mortar. *ASuW*:1 5in (127mm) OTO Melara DP.
Sensors:	*Surveillance*: SPS-501, SPQ-2D. *Fire control*: WM-22, (2). *Sonars*: SQS-505, SQS-505 VDS, SQS-501.
Complement:	285.

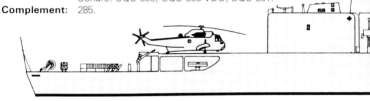

Above: *Athabaskan* (foreground) and *Algonquin* with the supply ship *Protecteur*. The two destroyers belong to the Canadian First Destroyer Squadron and operate in the Atlantic. In time of war their primary task would be the protection of NATO's shipping lanes.

Right: Particularly prominent in this overhead view of *Iroquois* are the canted uptakes for the gas turbines, and the broad double hangar, which accommodates two Sea King anti-submarine helicopters. The SQS-505 variable-depth sonar is housed in a deep stern well. Forward of the well is the large hatch cover for the Limbo ASW mortar.

The design of these ships is derived from a class of eight area defence "missile frigates" projected for the Canadian Navy in the early 1960s. In the event the expense of the Tartar missile system they were to have carried proved to be prohibitive, and the ships were redesigned with a large hangar and flight deck capable of supporting two CH-124 Sea King helicopters. The other ASW weapons systems are identical to those of the Annapolis class with the exception of the SQS-505 sonar, which is an advanced model employing two similar ▶

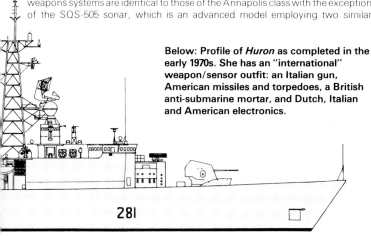

Below: Profile of *Huron* as completed in the early 1970s. She has an "international" weapon/sensor outfit: an Italian gun, American missiles and torpedoes, a British anti-submarine mortar, and Dutch, Italian and American electronics.

281

▶ transducers, one of which is hull-mounted and the other housed in the towed body of a variable-depth sonar.

In addition to their formidable anti-submarine capabilities these ships have weapons systems to defend them against light air or surface attack. There is an OTO Melara 127mm automatic DP gun on the forecastle, and the large "box" structure forward of the bridge houses the magazine and launcher arms of a Canadian Sea Sparrow short-range air defence system. Fire control for Sea Sparrow and for the 127mm gun mounting is provided by two HSA M 22 tracking radars, housed within GRP radomes. The SPS-501 air surveillance radar is essentially the US SPS-12 but with a Dutch LW-03 high-gain antenna; the secondary radar system, the SPQ-2D, is of Italian origin. Data is co-ordinated by a CCS 280 action information system.

These ships were the first destroyers built in the West with all-gas-turbine propulsion. The decision to adopt gas turbines was taken relatively late in the design process (the missile frigates were to have had steam propulsion) and was prompted by manning considerations. Unusually, the four propulsion units are mounted side by side; the FT 4 main power turbines are inboard with the F 12 cruise turbines outside them. The exhaust uptakes are led into a pair of canted funnels designed to keep the hot, corrosive gases clear of the flight deck and the radar antennae. The main propulsion turbines and the gearing are raft-mounted to reduce vibration. Gas-turbine generators and a passive-tank stabilisation system contribute to a very low acoustic signature, thereby improving sonar performance and making the ships less detectable by submarines.

The Iroquois class are shortly to undergo a major modernisation known as

Left: *Iroquois* underway in the North Atlantic. Note the "box" magazine housing for Canadian Sea Sparrow abaft the OTO Melara 127mm gun. The twin HSA WM-22 fire control radars can control both the gun and the missiles. The large Dutch LW-03 air search antenna is matched with the electronics of the American SPS-12 radar. A feature of all Canadian destroyers is the prominence accorded to sea-keeping. The Iroquois class combines high freeboard with a broad beam, which makes the ships dry and steady. Note the hinged cover for the anchor well; this helps to prevent damage in heavy seas, and enables the ships to operate in icy conditions. Numerous other ice-protection features are incorporated in this and other classes serving with the Royal Canadian Navy.

TRUMP (Tribal Update and Modernisation Programme), to fit them for the area defence mission. Modifications proposed include the replacement of the 127mm OTO gun by a Martin-Marietta Mk 41 vertical launch system for Standard SM-2 missiles. The Sea Sparrow magazine forward of the bridge will be replaced by a 76mm (3in) OTO Melara Compact Gun, and a Phalanx CIWS gun will be mounted atop the hangar. A completely new above-water sensor outfit will be installed, including Dutch LW-08 and DA-08 surveillance radars, and a STIR 1.8 fire control radar which will serve both the Standard missiles and the 76mm gun. New tactical data displays and advanced communications and data links will be installed to enable the ships to serve as task force flagships. The ASW weapons systems will remain essentially unchanged, although there will be a new torpedo-handling system.

The refits will take 18 months, with the first ship scheduled to be taken in hand in late 1986; the programme is due to be completed in 1991. In addition to the TRUMP modifications, the Pratt and Whitney F 12 cruise turbines will be replaced by a new model manufactured by Detroit Allison, and all turbine uptakes will be brought together in a single massive funnel.

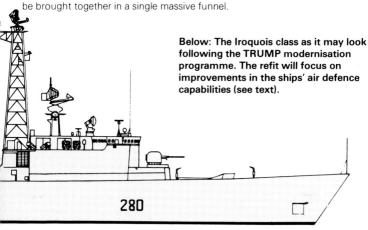

Below: The Iroquois class as it may look following the TRUMP modernisation programme. The refit will focus on improvements in the ships' air defence capabilities (see text).

Annapolis class

Completed:	1964.
Names:	265 *Annapolis*; 266 *Nipigon*.
Displacement:	2,400 tons standard; 3,000 tons full load.
Dimensions:	Length 371ft (113.1m) oa; beam 42ft (12.8m); draught 14ft 6in (4.4m).
Propulsion:	2-shaft English-Electric geared steam turbines; 30,000shp = 28kt.
Weapons:	*AAW*: 2 3in (76mm, 1 × 2) Mk 33 DP. *ASW*: 1 Sea King CH-124 helicopter; 2 triple Mk 32 tubes for Mk 44/46 torpedoes; 1 Mk 10 Limbo mortar.
Sensors:	*Surveillance*: SPS-12, SPS-10, Sperry Mk 2. *Fire control*: SPG-48. *Sonars*: SQS-503, SQS-504 VDS, SQS-501.
Complement:	228.

Annapolis and *Nipigon,* ordered in 1959, were the final two units in the 20-ship St. Laurent series, which encompassed four different sub-groups. While the hull-form and machinery were identical to those of earlier ships in the series, a radically new armament was fitted, and the upperworks were substantially redesigned.

These were the first Canadian ships of destroyer size designed from the outset to operate a manned helicopter capable of independent ASW operations. The centre part of the ship is dominated by a flight deck and hangar for the single CH-124 Sea King helicopter. In order to create sufficient space aft for a Limbo anti-submarine mortar the funnel uptakes were divided, allowing the hangar to be extended between them. Triple Mk 32 torpedo tubes are located beneath the flight deck. In addition to the SQS-503 and SQS-501 hull-mounted sonars, the ships were given an SQS-504 variable-depth sonar on a modified stern. Only one twin 3in mounting was fitted, the US Mk 33 model being preferred to the 70cal. British model fitted in earlier ships of the series because of weight considerations. The surveillance radars are carried on a tall plated foremast, while the ECM and TACAN antennae are mounted atop short pole masts around and between the twin funnels.

Mackenzie class

Completed:	1962–63.
Names:	261 *Mackenzie*; 262 *Saskatchewan*; 263 *Yukon*; 264 *Qu'Appelle*.
Displacement:	2,380 tons standard; 2,890 tons full load.
Dimensions:	Length 371ft (113.1m) oa; beam 42ft (12.8m); draught 13ft 6in (4.1m).
Propulsion:	2-shaft English-Electric geared steam turbines; 30,000shp = 28kt.
Weapons:	*AAW*: 4 3in (76mm, 2 × 2) Mk 6/Mk 33 DP. *ASW*: 2 Mk 10 Limbo mortars; 2 triple Mk 32 tubes for Mk 44/46 torpedoes.
Sensors:	*Surveillance*: SPS-12, SPS-10. *Fire control*: SPG-48, SPG-34. *Sonars*: SQS-505, SQS-501.
Complement:	210.

The four destroyers of the Mackenzie class, ordered in 1957, were essentially a repeat of the Restigouche class, with improvements in habitability, and bridge and weather-deck fittings better suited to cold-weather operations. They re-

Above: *Nipigon* (right) alongside a destroyer of the Iroquois class, following a NATO exercise in the North Atlantic.

Both ships now have the Litton CSS 280 tactical data system. They are currently undergoing an extensive DELEX (Destroyer Life Extension) refit which will involve the replacement of the SPS-12 air surveillance radar by a CMR-1820 with Plessey AWS-4 antenna, new fire control and navigational radars, and new ECM. The SQS-503 hull sonar will be replaced by the SQS-505 model fitted in the Iroquois class.

---

mained unmodified except for the fitting of triple Mk 32 torpedo tubes until the early 1980s, when all four ships underwent DELEX overhauls. An SQS-505 hull sonar replaced the original SQS-503 and there was some updating of the electronics.

The Mackenzies, allocated to the Pacific Training Group, will remain in service until 1990–93.

Below: *Mackenzie* in the late 1960s. Two out of the four ships of this class retain the British 3in/70 Mk 6 mounting forward.

Restigouche class

Completed:	1958–59.
Names:	236 *Gatineau*; 257 *Restigouche*; 258 *Kootenay*; 259 *Terra Nova*.
Displacement:	2,390 tons standard; 2,900 tons full load.
Dimensions:	Length 371ft (113.1m) oa; beam 42ft (12.8m); draught 14ft (4.3m).
Propulsion:	2-shaft English-Electric geared steam turbines; 30,000shp = 28kt.
Weapons:	*AAW*: 1 4-cell launcher for Sea Sparrow; 2 3in (76mm, 1 × 2) Mk 6 DP. *ASW*: 1 8-cell launcher Mk 16 for ASROC (8 reloads); 1 Mk 10 Limbo mortar.
Sensors:	*Surveillance*: SPS-12 or CM-1820, SPS-10, Sperry Mk 2. *Fire control*: SPG-48. *Sonars*: SQS-503, SQS-505 VDS, SQS-501.
Complement:	285.

The Restigouche class, ordered in 1952, was derived from the St. Laurent design, but a British 3in/70cal. Mk 6 mounting replaced the US-model 3in/50cal. Mk 33 forward of the bridge. The after Mk 33 mounting was retained. In the mid-1960s it was decided to update all seven ships by fitting ASROC in place of the after gun mounting and one of the two Mk 10 Limbo mortars. *Terra Nova* completed her refit in 1968, *Gatineau* followed in 1972, and *Kootenay* and *Restigouche* recommissioned in 1973. In addition to the fitting of ASROC, an SQS-505 variable-depth sonar was installed, a small launcher for Canadian Sea Sparrow was fitted abaft the funnel, and the original plated foremast was replaced by a tall lattice mast. Budgetary constraints prevented the extension of these modifications to the remaining three units of the class, and *Chaudière* (DDE 235), *Columbia* (DDE 260) and *St. Croix* (DDE 256) were duly placed in reserve in 1974.

The four converted ships serve in the Pacific, and are currently undergoing DELEX overhauls to prolong their service life until 1991–94. They are receiving similar modifications to the Annapolis class: the CMR-1820 air surveillance radar and a new fire control system will be fitted, and communications and ECM capabilities will be upgraded. *Terra Nova* evaluated the MEL CANEWS electronic support measures (ESM) system in 1982–83.

Left: A recent view of *Kootenay:* ASROC and a launcher for Canadian Sea Sparrow missiles have replaced the after gun mounting and one of the two Mk 10 Limbo mortars, and she has been fitted with a lattice foremast similar to that of the Iroquois class. The four surviving ships of the Restigouche class serve in the Pacific, and are currently undergoing DELEX refits to prolong their service lives.

Below: *Terra Nova* in her original configuration. She has the British 3in/70 Mk 6 forward and a US 3in/50 Mk 33 in an open mounting aft. The large watertight hatch on the quarterdeck conceals two British Mk 10 Limbo anti-submarine mortars.

CANADA

St. Laurent class

Completed:	1955–57.
Names:	206 *Saguenay*; 207 *Skeena*; 229 *Ottawa*; 230 *Margaree* 233 *Fraser*; 234 *Assiniboine*.
Displacement:	2,260 tons standard; 2,860 tons full load.
Dimensions:	Length 371ft (113.1m) oa; beam 42ft (12.8m); draught 13ft 3in (4.2m).
Propulsion:	2-shaft English-Electric geared steam turbines; 30,000shp = 28kt.
Weapons:	*AAW*: 2 3in (76mm, 1 × 2) Mk 33 DP. *ASW*: 1 Sea King CH-124 helicopter; 2 triple Mk 32 tubes for Mk 44/46 torpedoes; 1 Mk 10 Limbo mortar.
Sensors:	*Surveillance*: SPS-12, SPS-10. *Fire control*: SPG-48. *Sonars*: SQS-503, SQS-504 VDS, SQS-501.
Complement:	228.

The original design for these ships dates from 1949, when there was a pressing NATO requirement for anti-submarine escorts to protect merchant shipping in the North Atlantic. The design was derived from that of the British Type 12 frigate, but although overall dimensions and the machinery were identical, a number of modifications were made to conform to Canadian operational requirements and defence procurement policy. As completed the ships had two

British Limbo ASW mortars, two twin US 3in Mk 33 DP mountings, and two single 40mm AA. The electronics outfit was of US origin.

Like their British counterparts, the St. Laurent class proved to be excellent seaboats, but their short-range anti-submarine weapons were quickly rendered obsolescent by the advent of the nuclear-powered submarine. It was therefore decided at the end of the 1950s that they should undergo an extensive rebuild on the pattern of *Annapolis* and *Nipigon,* which were on order at this time. The refit involved the deletion of one Limbo mortar and all the after guns, and their replacement by a large hangar and flight deck for a CH-124 Sea King helicopter. The funnel uptakes were divided, as in the Annapolis class, in order to accommodate the forward end of the hangar. Triple Mk 32 torpedo tubes were added beneath the flight deck and an SQS-504 variable-depth sonar fitted, but the above-water sensors remained the same. The conversions began in 1961 and were completed between 1963 and 1966.

St. Laurent (DDH 205) decommissioned in 1974, but the other six ships remain in first-line service. In 1980–81 all six underwent DELEX overhauls, designed to extend their service life by minor updating of electronics and by carrying out essential repairs to the hulls and machinery. They are expected to decommission between 1987 and 1990, by which time the construction of the new frigates will be well advanced.

Below: *Skeena* refuels from the US Navy replenishment oiler *Milwaukee* (AOR-2) while assigned to NATO's Standing Naval Force Atlantic (STANAVFORLANT). Although extensively modernised during the 1960s, these destroyers are now 30 years old and are overdue for replacement.

Almirante Riveros class

Completed: 1960.
Names: D 18 *Almirante Riveros*; D 19 *Almirante Williams*.
Displacement: 2,730 tons standard; 3,300 tons full load.
Dimensions: Length 402ft (122.5m) oa; beam 43ft (13.1m);
draught 12ft 9in (3.9m).
Propulsion: 2-shaft Parsons-Pamatreda geared steam turbines;
50,000shp = 34.5kt.
Weapons: *AAW*: 2 quadruple launchers for Seacat; 4 4in (102mm) DP;
4 40mm (4 × 1) AA.
ASuW: 2 MM38 Exocet missiles.
ASW: 2 Squid mortars; 2 triple Mk 32 tubes for Mk 44/46
torpedoes.
Sensors: *Surveillance*: Plessey AWS-1, Marconi SNW-10.
Fire control: SRG-102 (2), SNG-20 (2), SWW-20.
Sonars: Type 164B.
Complement: 266.

In 1955, at a time when most South American countries were content to purchase US war-built destroyers which were surplus to requirements, the Chilean Navy took the unusual step of ordering new purpose-built vessels from the British Vickers-Armstrong shipyard. The hull and propulsion machinery are essentially those of the Royal Navy's Daring class, but slim tapered funnels and a conical, tapered foremast give the Chilean vessels a more elegant profile.

A new automatic single 4in dual-purpose mounting was developed specifically for this class by Vickers. This put the ships very much in line with contemporary European developments (cf. the French *La Galissonnière* as originally designed and the German Hamburg class). Six single 40mm AA mountings were fitted on a platform deck which extended aft from the break in the forecastle, and there was a quintuple bank of torpedo tubes abaft the second funnel. A small air search radar was located atop the plated foremast, with a large target indication radar similar in configuration to the British Type 992Q below it, and there were radar directors for the 4in mountings fore and aft. Dutch M-4 FC radars were fitted for the 40mm mountings.

In 1964, shortly after completion, quadruple launchers for Seacat surface-to-air missiles were fitted in place of the after 40mm mountings. Both ships subsequently underwent a major modernisation at the British Swan Hunter shipyard between 1971 and 1975. Four MM38 Exocet anti-ship missile launchers were fit-

Above: *Almirante Riveros* as completed by Vickers in 1960, with six 40mm AA mountings amidships and a quintuple bank of 533mm tubes.

ted in place of the torpedo tubes, and a new outfit of above-water sensors was installed, including a Plessey AWS-1 air surveillance radar (carried atop a new plated mainmast) and US WLR-1 electronic countermeasures equipment. Two of the four Exocet launchers were removed from each ship in 1980 for installation aboard ex-US Navy destroyers of the Allen M. Sumner class.

Below: A recent view of *Almirante Riveros,* now with the Plessey AWS-1 air surveillance antenna atop a slim plated mainmast, and a new target indication radar atop the foremast. The electronics outfit of both ships was updated at the Swan Hunter shipyard between 1971 and 1975. Triple Mk 32 tubes for Mk 46 ASW torpedoes and four single launchers for MM38 Exocet anti-ship missiles were fitted during the ships' modernisation. Two of the four Exocet launchers have since been removed. The 4in gun mountings have a range of 12,500 yds and can be elevated to an angle of 75 degrees.

Luda class

Completed:	1972.
Names:	105, 106, 107, 108, 109, 110, 111, 131, 132, 161, 162, 163, 164, 165.
Displacement:	2,950–3,250 tons standard; 3,900 tons full load.
Dimensions:	Length 430ft (131m) oa; beam 45ft (13.7m); draught 15ft (4.6m) max.
Propulsion:	2-shaft geared steam turbines; 60,000shp = 32kt.
Weapons:	*AAW*: 8 37mm (4 × 2) AA, 4 25mm (2 × 2) AA. *ASuW*: 2 triple launchers for CSS-N-2 missiles; 4 5.1in (130mm, 2 × 2) DP. *ASW*: 2 12-barrelled FQF-2500 rocket launchers; 4 BMB-1/2 depth charge mortars; 2 depth charge racks.
Sensors:	*Surveillance*: Bean Sticks or Pea Sticks, Fin Curve. *Fire control*: Square Tie, Sun Visor. *Sonars*: 1 hull-mounted HF.
Complement:	340–350.

Named after the Chinese shipyard at which construction was first observed, this class is derived from the Soviet Kotlin. It is thought that plans of the Soviet design were in Chinese hands by 1957–58, but it was to be another ten years before the first Chinese unit was laid down, probably because of technical problems and a shortage of skilled engineering personnel in the shipyards.

The Luda has a slightly larger hull than the Kotlin, and a squared-off transom similar to that of later Soviet designs was adopted. There are twin 130mm dual-purpose guns fore and aft, as in the Soviet ships, but in place of the quintuple torpedo tubes of the original Kotlin design there are triple launchers for CSS-N-1 anti-ship missiles. The CSS-N-1·is a Chinese derivative of the Soviet SS-N-2 Styx horizon-range missile. One unit (No. 131) has been observed with four twin 57mm water-cooled mountings, but the Chinese appear to have experienced problems with this model, as all other units are now fitted with twin 37mm mountings.

The anti-submarine systems carried are particularly primitive, comprising a high-frequency hull sonar and hand-loaded rocket launchers derived from early Soviet models. The air surveillance and fire control radars are equally primitive, and in the early 1980s tentative approaches were made to the British defence industry to provide the Ludas with modern air defence weapons and advanced electronics. Proposals to fit the ship with Sea Dart were actively discussed before the Chinese withdrew from negotiations, partly on grounds of cost but also because of fears of dependence on Western defence technology.

Above: A destroyer of the Luda class launches a Hai Ying 2 surface-to-surface missile. The Chinese missile is derived from the Soviet SS-N-2 Styx, which has an effective range of less than 20nm.

Above: The Luda class is equipped with a number of elderly weapons systems, but the ships' greatest weakness is undoubtedly their electronics. The surveillance and fire control radars are derived from Soviet models which date from the 1950s, and there are no modern ECM or anti-missile systems. A proposed air defence modernisation of the ships, based on the installation of the British Sea Dart system, was not proceeded with.

Left: The Luda is basically an enlarged Kotlin, with triple launchers for anti-ship missiles in place of the quintuple torpedo tubes mounted in the original Kotlin design. The construction of the Chinese destroyers has been delayed by technological problems and a shortage of skilled shipyard labour.

Cassard class

Completed:	1988 onwards.
Names:	*Cassard* (+ 1 building).
Displacement:	3,820 tons standard; 4,340 tons full load.
Dimensions:	Length 456ft (139m) oa; beam 46ft (14m); draught 18ft (5.5m).
Propulsion:	2 shafts; 4 SEMT-Pielstick 18 PA 6 BTC diesels; 42,300bhp = 29.5kt.
Weapons:	*AAW*: 1 single Mk 13 launcher for Standard SM-1 MR (40 missiles); 2 six-barrelled launchers for SADRAL; 1 3.9in (100mm) DP; 2 20mm (2 × 1) AA.
	ASuW: 2 quadruple MM40 Exocet missiles; 1 SA.365F Dauphin 2 helicopter.
	ASW: 2 catapults for L5 torpedoes (10).
Sensors:	*Surveillance*: DRBJ-11B, DRBV-26.
	Fire control: SPG-51C (2), DRBC-33.
	Sonars: DUBA-25.
Complement:	241.

These ships are designed to replace the air defence conversions of the T47 type (see *Du Chayla*). They share a common hull with the Georges Leygues class, and are referred to as the C70 AA type, but only a limited degree of standardisation has been possible because of the very different weapon and sensor outfits.

The choice of an all-diesel propulsion system in preference to the CODOG arrangement of the Georges Leygues class was dictated by a requirement for more centre-line space to accommodate the air defence systems; the installation of gas turbines would have meant extensive intake and uptake trunking and hot exhaust gases, which would have precluded fitting the DRBJ-11B target designation radar amidships.

The Mk 13 launchers and missile fire control systems will be transferred direct from the T47s as they are retired from service. According to the initial design the ships would have had a second single 100mm mounting aft, but it has now been decided to fit a small hangar for a Dauphin SA.365F helicopter armed with AS-15 anti-ship missiles. Six-barrelled launchers for SADRAL close-range air defence missiles, which employ infra-red guidance, will be mounted on each side of the hangar. Quadruple launchers for MM40 Exocet missiles will be fitted amidships, and particular attention has been paid to electronic countermeasures, with both Sagaie and Dagaie chaff launchers being installed.

No anti-submarine weapons other than the catapults for L5 torpedoes are fitted, and the hull sonar is an austere medium-frequency model, the DUBA-25. However, the space beneath the helicopter deck will eventually accommodate the DSBV-61 towed array.

The Cassard class will be fitted with Syracuse satellite communications terminals, and will have a SENIT 6 tactical data system. A new gun fire control radar, the DRBC-33, will be fitted, and will be accompanied on the third and fourth units by the new 100mm "compact" gun.

Financial constraints have considerably delayed the programme, and the first ship will not now enter service before 1988, by which time all four units of the T47 class will have decommissioned.

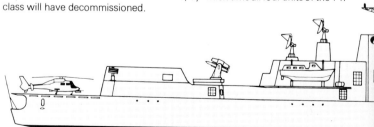

Above: The official model of *Cassard,* with an SA.365F Dauphin 2 helicopter on the flight deck aft.

Above: The hull of the first of the Cassard class under construction at the Lorient Naval Dockyard. These ships have been delayed by financial constraints, and now feature a permanent helicopter hangar. The Standard missile systems are being transferred from the Du Chayla class.

Below: Profile of *Cassard.* Note the SADRAL missile launchers abreast the helicopter hangar.

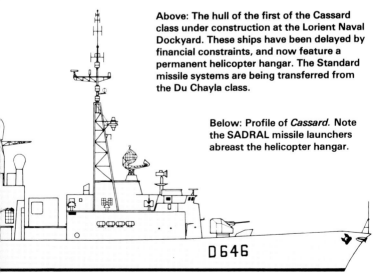

D 646

Georges Leygues class

Completed:	1979 onwards.
Names:	D 640 *Georges Leygues*; D 641 *Dupleix*; D 642 *Montcalm*; D 643 *Jean De Vienne*; D 644 *Primauguet* (building); D 645 *La Motte-Piquet* (building).
Displacement:	3,830 tons standard; 4,170 tons full load.
Dimensions:	Length 456ft (139m) oa; beam 46ft (14m); draught 18ft 9in (5.7m) max.
Propulsion:	2-shaft CODOG; 2 Olympus TM3B gas turbines, 52,000hp = 30kt; 2 SEMT-Pielstick 16 PA 6 diesels, 10,400bhp = 21kt.
Weapons:	*AAW*: 1 8-cell launcher for Crotale (26 missiles); 1 3.9in (100mm) DP; 2 20mm (2 × 1) AA. *ASuW*: 4 MM38 Exocet missiles (D 640–41); 4–8 MM40 Exocet missiles (D 642 onwards). *ASW*: 2 WG.13 Lynx helicopters; 2 catapults for L5 torpedoes (10).
Sensors:	*Surveillance*: DRBV-26, DRBV-51C. *Fire control*: DRBV-51G, DRBC-32D. *Sonars*: DUBV-23, DUBV-43 VDS.
Complement:	216.

The C70 design is a smaller, less costly development of the Tourville (F67) class. The major innovation lies in the propulsion machinery, which employs Rolls-Royce Olympus TM3B gas turbines to drive the ships at a maximum speed of 30kt. Although the ships are similar in size to the Type 42 destroyers of the Royal Navy and the Dutch Standaard-class frigates, both of which have the basic Olympus/Tyne COGOG arrangement, the French rejected the Tyne as a cruise turbine because it was considered to lack sufficient power for running astern, particularly in the tropics, and also because of its relatively high fuel consumption. Instead the Georges Leygues class has two SEMT-Pielstick diesels linked with the Olympus turbines in a CODOG arrangement. The machinery layout is otherwise identical to that of the British and Dutch vessels, with the main propulsion units grouped centrally in adjacent compartments, and the auxiliary machinery rooms fore and aft.

The adoption of gas turbines, which require extensive intake and uptake trunking, in a hull some 45ft (14m) shorter than that of the Tourville class placed severe limitations on the space available amidships for weapons systems. A choice had to be made, therefore, between the Malafon anti-submarine missile and manned helicopters. Malafon was discarded, and the ships have a large double hangar aft for two WG.13 Lynx helicopters, with handling facilities identical to those of the Tourville class. The reduction in centre-line length meant that there was space for only a single 100mm mounting, and only four MM38 Exocet missiles are fitted in the early ships. The catapults for L5 torpedoes are installed in the after end of the bridge structure.

Georges Leygues was fitted with the second prototype Crotale surface-to-air missile launcher (the first was fitted in the trials ship *Ile d'Oléron*). In addition to the eight missiles carried in the launcher, 18 reloads are stored in the deckhouse ▶

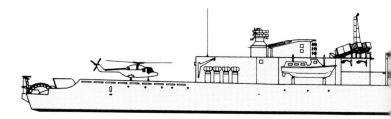

Above: *Georges Leygues,* first of the C70 type *corvettes.* She and her five sisters constitute the anti-submarine variant of the design.

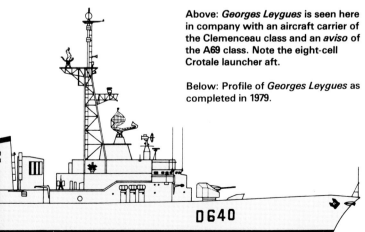

Above: *Georges Leygues* is seen here in company with an aircraft carrier of the Clemenceau class and an *aviso* of the A69 class. Note the eight-cell Crotale launcher aft.

Below: Profile of *Georges Leygues* as completed in 1979.

D 640

Above: *Montcalm,* the first of the class to receive the MM40 variant of Exocet. The adoption of folding fins for the missile means that two can be carried in place of a single MM38, for a total of eight.

Below: *Jean de Vienne,* the latest of the class, has Dagaie chaff launchers in place of the elderly Syllex, and Syracuse satellite communication radomes. These will be retrofitted in all ships.

▶ on which it is mounted; they are hoisted through a hatch in the sloping deckhead and are loaded by hand. The missiles can be fired either from the ship's command centre or from a fire control compartment directly beneath the launcher. Target designation is provided by a DRBV-51 radar, the antenna for which is located on the aft-facing platform of the lattice foremast. The sensor outfit installed in the first four units of the class is identical to that of the Tourville class, although the action information system is the SENIT 4, which is based on more advanced computers with all-French components.

The C70 type was to have been built in relatively large numbers to replace the older French destroyers of the T47 and T53 classes, but financial constraints have slowed the rate of construction and only six units of the class will be built (a seventh unit, D 646, has been cancelled). From *Montcalm* onwards, two quadruple MM40 Exocet launchers are replacing the four single MM38 launchers, and *Jean De Vienne* has Dagaie chaff launchers in place of Syllex. Syracuse satellite communications terminals are now being retrofitted in all units. The last two ships, D 644 and D 645, will have a number of important modifications, including the DSBV-61 towed linear passive array, a higher bridge, an improved version of Crotale, the 100mm ''compact'' mounting, and a DRBV-15 multi-mode radar (currently being fitted in *Aconit*) in place of both the DRBV-26 air surveillance and the DRBV-51 target designation radar.

Tourville class

Completed:	1974–77.
Names:	D 610 *Tourville*; D 611 *Duguay-Trouin*; D 612 *De Grasse*.
Displacement:	4,800 tons standard; 5,800 tons full load.
Dimensions:	Length 501ft (152.5m) oa; beam 50ft (15.3m); draught 21ft 3in (6.5m) max.
Propulsion:	2-shaft Rateau geared steam turbines; 54,400shp = 31kt.
Weapons:	*AAW*: 1 8-cell launcher for Crotale (26 missiles); 2 3.9in (100mm, 2 × 1) DP; 2 20mm (2 × 1) AA.
	ASuW: 6 MM38 Exocet missiles.
	ASW: 2 WG.13 Lynx helicopters; 1 single launcher for Malafon (13 missiles); 2 catapults for L5 torpedoes (10).
Sensors:	*Surveillance*: DRBV-26, DRBV-51B.
	Fire control: DRBV-51G, DRBC-32D.
	Sonars: DUBV-23, DUBV-43 VDS.
Complement:	282.

Above: *De Grasse,* flagship of the French Atlantic Squadron. She is the last of the large *frégates* built for the Marine Nationale during the 1960s and 1970s. Financial difficulties arising from France's continued commitment to a submarine-based nuclear deterrent plus conventional "intervention forces" have severely curtailed the construction of large surface vessels, and the Suffren and Tourville classes have been superseded by ships of more modest dimensions.

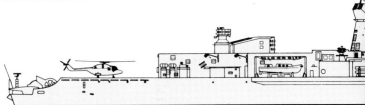

Above: *Tourville,* the first of the class. She was completed with a third 100mm gun on the hangar roof, but this has now been replaced by Crotale. Note the six single MM38 Exocet launchers amidships.

These three ships were originally to have been built to the same design as *Aconit.* However, dissatisfaction with the single-shaft arrangement of the latter vessel led to a doubling-up of the machinery installation, resulting in a 4kt increase in speed, and helicopter handling and maintenance facilities were added, resulting in an altogether larger and more capable vessel. Initially designated *corvettes,* the ships were reclassified as *frégates* while building, and the pennant numbers were changed accordingly.

These were the first French ships of destroyer size designed from the outset to operate anti-submarine helicopters. The large double hangar can accommodate two WG.13 Lynx helicopters side by side and is served by a rail-type transfer system which crosses the flight deck. In the centre of the landing area there is a grille associated with the Harpoon securing device.

In addition to the helicopters the ships have a Malafon missile launcher amidships. Unlike the arrangement in the Suffren and Aconit classes the launcher is mounted forward of the funnel, and the reload magazine is located in a deckhouse which extends from the after end of the bridge structure. Atop the magazine are six single launchers for MM38 Exocet anti-ship missiles. The catapults for the L5 ASW torpedoes are fitted in the deckhouse immediately abaft the funnel. The sonar outfit is identical to that of *Aconit,* and target data is co-ordinated by the same SENIT 3 action information system.

The Tourville class was designed to carry the Crotale short-range air defence system, which was then at an early stage of development. *Tourville* and *Duguay-Trouin* were completed with a third 100mm mounting atop the hangar as a temporary measure, but this was removed in 1980 and 1979 respectively, when the Crotale system was installed. *De Grasse* was completed without the third 100mm mounting, and received Crotale in 1981.

As originally designed the Tourville class was to have received an above-water sensor outfit identical to that of *Aconit.* However, while the ships were under construction it was decided to fit the new long-range DRBV-26 radar in place of ▶

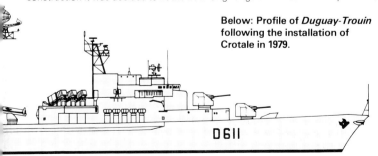

Below: Profile of *Duguay-Trouin* following the installation of Crotale in 1979.

D 611

▶ the DRBV-22A for air surveillance, and the DRBV-13 multi-mode radar was replaced by a DRBV-51B target designation radar for Crotale.

De Grasse was modified while building to burn distillate fuel, and *Tourville* was similarly modified during her Crotale refit in 1980. The only future modification currently planned is the replacement of the ageing Syllex chaff launchers, which are a French version of the British Corvus, by the Dagaie system.

The Tourvilles are generally regarded as successful ships, although longitudinal stresses in the hull led to the fitting of additional strakes of steel plating immediately below the level of the upper deck in the late 1970s. Two pairs of stabilisers contribute to a steady ship, and seaworthiness is on a par with the Suffren class. All three units serve in the Atlantic Squadron, together with *Aconit* and a number of older fleet escorts of the D'Estrées and Du Chayla classes. Following completion and work-up, *De Grasse* replaced *Duperré* as

flagship of the Atlantic Squadron, the primary mission of which is to conduct independent anti-submarine operations in the North Atlantic, either in a NATO context or in defence of French national interests.

Below: A recent view of *Duguay-Trouin,* newly fitted with Syracuse satellite communications radomes. The large air surveillance aerial is a DRBV-26, and the smaller antenna above it belongs to the DRBV-51B target designation radar for Crotale. The DRBV-51G guidance radar for Crotale is mounted on the launcher itself, between the two quadruple groups of missile canisters. Fire control for the two single 100mm dual-purpose guns is provided by a DRBC-32D radar, which is located atop the bridge structure. In common with her sister-ships, *Duguay-Trouin* is fitted with the SENIT 3 action information system.

Aconit class

Completed:	1973.
Names:	D 609 *Aconit*.
Displacement:	3,500 tons standard; 3,840 tons full load.
Dimensions:	Length 417ft (127m) oa; beam 44ft (13.4m); draught 19ft (5.8m) max.
Propulsion:	1-shaft Rateau geared steam turbine; 28,650shp = 27kt.
Weapons:	*AAW*: 2 3.9in (100mm, 2 × 1) DP.
	ASuW: 2 quadruple launchers for MM40 Exocet missiles.
	ASW: 1 single launcher for Malafon (13 missiles); 2 catapults for L5 torpedoes (10).
Sensors:	*Surveillance*: DRBV-15, DRBV-22A.
	Fire control: DRBC-32B.
	Sonars: DUBV-23, DUBV-43 VDS.
Complement:	232.

Aconit was to have been the first of a class of five anti-submarine *corvettes*. Unlike the ships of the Suffren class, which were designed as carrier escorts, the *corvettes* were intended for independent ASW operations in the North Atlantic. Since the primary mission was the protection of merchant shipping, fleet speed was not a requirement. A single-shaft machinery installation was therefore adopted, producing 28,650shp for a maximum speed of 27kt.

The anti-submarine systems installed were those tested aboard the trials ship *La Galissonnière* (see *D'Estrées* entry). The Malafon missile launcher is amidships, with the reload magazine located inside the after deckhouse. A quadruple 305mm ASW mortar was originally fitted forward of the bridge, but this has recently been replaced by two quadruple launchers for MM40 Exocet missiles. Catapults for L5 ASW torpedoes are housed inside the after deckhouse. Paired DUBV-23 hull-mounted and DUBV-43 variable-depth sonars are fitted, and anti-submarine operations are co-ordinated by a SENIT 3 tactical data system specially designed for this class.

Although *Aconit* has no surface-to-air missile system she was fitted with extensive air surveillance radar systems, including the DRBV-13 multi-mode pulse-doppler radar housed beneath a distinctive radome. This was the only example of the model produced, and it is currently being replaced by a DRBV-15.

The French Navy was not entirely happy with the single shaft, and the design was quickly overtaken by other developments, notably the manned ASW helicopter. The other units of the class were therefore completed to a new design (see *Tourville* entry).

Below: An aerial view of *Aconit* in 1984, following the removal of her quadruple 305mm anti-submarine mortar from its former position between the bridge and the forward 100mm dual-purpose gun. The mortar has now been replaced by two groups each of four canisters for MM40 Exocet anti-ship missiles. The distinctive radome now houses a DRBV-15 pulse-doppler radar.

Suffren class

Completed:	1967–70.
Names:	D 602 *Suffren*; D 603 *Duquesne*.
Displacement:	5,090 tons standard; 6,090 tons full load.
Dimensions:	Length 517ft (157.6m) oa; beam 51ft (15.5m); draught 23ft 9in (7.25m) max.
Propulsion:	2-shaft Rateau geared steam turbines; 72,500shp = 34kt.
Weapons:	*AAW*: 1 twin launcher for Masurca (48 missiles); 2 3.9in (100mm, 2 × 1) DP; 4 20mm (4 × 1) AA.
	ASuW: 4 MM38 Exocet missiles.
	ASW: 1 single launcher for Malafon (13 missiles); 2 catapults for L5 torpedoes (10).
Sensors:	*Surveillance*: DRBI-23, DRBV-50.
	Fire control: DRBR-51 (2), DRBC-32A.
	Sonars: DUBV-23, DUBV-43 VDS.
Complement:	355.

Above: *Duquesne* underway. Two Masurca surface-to-air missiles are in position on the twin-arm launcher aft, and there is a Malafon anti-submarine missile on the launch ramp amidships. The four single launchers for Exocet were fitted in 1976–77.

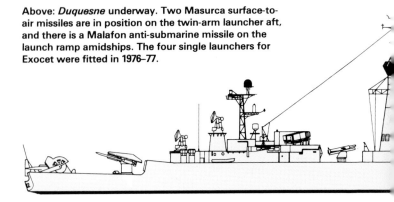

These were the first French destroyers designed from the outset to carry surface-to-air missiles. Authorised under the 1960–65 naval programme, they were intended to provide both air defence and anti-submarine protection for the new generation of French carriers. Three ships were initially projected, with more to follow later, but in the event budgetary problems resulted in only two being completed. The French Navy classifies them as *frégates lance-engins* (guided missile frigates).

In keeping with France's desire for political and military independence the weapons and sensors of the ships are exclusively of French design and manufacture. The principal missile system is Masurca, a medium-range SAM similar in configuration and in performance to the US Navy's Terrier. The magazine, which contains 48 rounds, is located in the hull immediately forward of the twin-arm launcher, which is mounted on the quarterdeck. Initial detection and target tracking is performed by the DRBI-23 multi-function radar, which is housed beneath a distinctive radome atop the bridge structure. The Masurca Mod.1 missile was a beam-rider, but the Mod.3 in current service employs semi-active guidance; two DRBR-51 tracker/illuminators are provided. Target data is co-ordinated by a SENIT 1 tactical data system, which also controls the air defence ▶

Below: *Suffren* as she appeared after her refit in 1979–80, when MM38 Exocet missiles were fitted atop the Malafon magazine and 20mm AA guns added forward and aft.

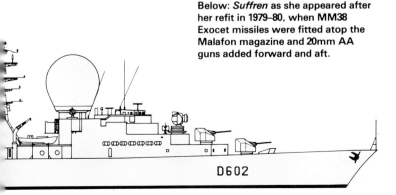

D602

▶ and ASW weapons. Three pairs of stabilisers are fitted, making the ships very steady missile platforms.

As with the Royal Navy's Type 82, which was designed for a similar mission, anti-submarine missiles were preferred to a manned ASW helicopter. The Suffrens received the Malafon system, which had previously undergone trials aboard the T56-class destroyer *La Galissonnière* (see *D'Estrées* entry). The launcher is amidships and the magazine, which holds 13 rounds, is immediately abaft it inside the after deckhouse. Target data is provided by paired DUBV-23 bow-mounted and DUBV-43 variable-depth sonars. A novel feature of these ships was the installation of fixed catapults for L5 anti-submarine torpedoes in place of the trainable torpedo mountings fitted in earlier ships. The catapults are located in the deckhouse forward of the central "mack", and each catapult is served by a rack holding five torpedoes.

The original armament was completed by two single 100mm mountings and two single 30mm AA mountings. In 1976–77, however, *Duquesne* was fitted with four MM38 Exocet launchers on the after deckhouse, and the single 30mm mountings were replaced by 20mm Oerlikons. Two further single Oerlikon

mountings were fitted forward abreast the DRBC-32A fire control director. *Suffren* was similarly modified in 1979–80. Future modifications planned include the replacement of the DRBC-32A FC radar by the digital DRBC-33 in 1987, and the replacement of the Syllex chaff launchers by Dagaie.

These ships introduced a new style of naval architecture to the French Navy. The hull-form, which is characterised by a clipper bow with negative sheer to enable the forward guns to fire at low angles of elevation, has been adopted not only for more recent French designs, but for a number of other West European vessels, notably the Dutch Standaard frigate and the Royal Navy's Type 23.

Suffren and *Duquesne* began their service careers with the Atlantic Squadron, but in 1975 they were transferred to the Mediterranean, together with the carriers *Foch* and *Clemenceau* and the cruiser *Colbert*.

Below: *Suffren* in 1983, following the installation of Exocet. The large, distinctive radome houses a DRBI-23 radar of French design and manufacture. It provides range and heightfinding data, and long-range tracking for the Masurca missile system.

FRANCE

D'Estrées / La Galissonnière / Duperré classes

Completed: 1956–62.
Names: D 627 *Maillé Brézé*; D 628 *Vauquelin*; D 629 *D'Estrées*; D 632 *Guépratte*. Also D 633 *Duperré*; D 638 *La Galissonnière*.
Displacement: 2,750 tons standard; 3,740 tons full load.
Dimensions: Length 434ft 6in (132.5m) oa; beam 42ft (12.7m); draught 19ft 3in (5.9m).
Propulsion: 2-shaft Rateau geared steam turbines; 63,000shp = 32kt.
Weapons: *AAW*: 2 3.9in (100mm, 2 × 1) DP.
ASW: 1 single launcher for Malafon (13 missiles); 1 6-barrelled 375mm mortar; 2 triple tubes for L3 torpedoes.
Sensors: *Surveillance*: DRBV-22A, DRBV-50.
Fire control: DRBC-32A.
Sonars: DUBV-23, DUBV-43 VDS.
Complement: 269.
Note: Data above applies to *D'Estrées*.

Above: *La Galissonnière* in 1983, the year in which she was transferred from the Mediterranean to the Atlantic Squadron. The photo gives an excellent view of the unusual helicopter-handling arrangements: the hangar sides fold down to form the flight deck for an Alouette III anti-submarine helicopter.

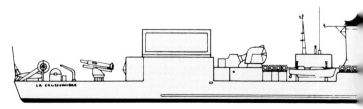

Above: *Vauquelin*, one of five vessels of the former Surcouf class to receive an extensive mid-life anti-submarine modernisation. Unlike *La Galissonnière* she carries no helicopter, but the abandonment of this feature has resulted in some improvement in the layout of other weapon systems, notably the guns and the ASW rocket launcher.

These ships all belong to the series of fleet escorts (*escorteurs d'escadre*) built to provide air defence for the French fleet in the postwar period. The T47 and T53 sub-groups, of twelve and five ships respectively, were conventional destroyers armed with three twin 5in (127mm) mountings, three twin 57mm AA mountings and four triple banks of torpedo tubes (for both anti-surface and anti-submarine work). The sixth of the T53 class, *La Galissonnière*, was completed to a revised design, which was subsequently designated T56.

Originally *La Galissonnière* was to have been a conventional air defence type armed with four of the new 100mm single automatic mountings, but the French Navy was by this time becoming more concerned with the threat posed to the carrier task forces by nuclear-powered submarines, and she was finally completed as a trials ship for a new generation of anti-submarine weapons and sensors. Only two of the four 100mm mountings were retained forward; in place of the after mountings was installed the prototype for the Malafon ASW missile. The deckhouse containing the missile magazine doubles as a helicopter flight deck atop which is installed a collapsible hangar for an Alouette helicopter. A 305mm quadruple anti-submarine mortar was initially fitted forward of the hangar, but this was removed in the late 1970s. Only the forward (short ASW) torpedo tubes were retained. *La Galissonnière* conducted trials for these new weapons systems and for the prototypes of the DUBV-23 hull-mounted and DUBV-43 variable-depth sonars for some years before she was finally incorporated into the active fleet. She served in the Mediterranean until 1983, when she transferred to the Atlantic Squadron.

Successful trials with *La Galissonnière* provided the impetus for the conver- ▶

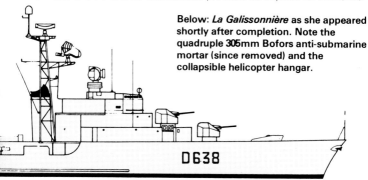

Below: *La Galissonnière* as she appeared shortly after completion. Note the quadruple 305mm Bofors anti-submarine mortar (since removed) and the collapsible helicopter hangar.

Above: *Maillé Brézé* in 1980. Note the triple anti-submarine torpedo tubes trained to port and the large DUBV-43 VDS.

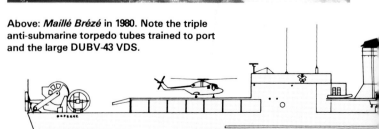

▶ sion of five ships of the T47 type to the anti-submarine configuration. The conversion was relatively austere; they received Malafon, but the somewhat improvised helicopter handling arrangements of *La Galissonnière* were not repeated. Instead the second of the 100mm mountings was installed atop the Malafon magazine, and a six-barrelled 375mm ASW rocket launcher was fitted in "B" position immediately forward of the bridge. Again, only the forward ASW torpedo tubes were retained. DUBV-23 and DUBV-43 sonars were installed, but unlike later purpose-built ASW vessels the ships have no SENIT action information system.

D'Estrées and *Guépratte* serve in the Mediterranean, *Maillé-Brézé* and *Vauquelin* in the Atlantic. The fifth ship, *Casabianca,* decommissioned in 1984, and the others will follow in the next few years as more units of the *Georges Leygues* class enter service.

Duperré is the sole survivor of the T53 sub-group. Following service as a sonar trials ship in the late 1960s, she too underwent an ASW refit, but re-entered service in 1974 to a much-modified design. Malafon and the second 100mm mounting were replaced by a large flight deck and hangar for a WG.13 Lynx helicopter, and four single launchers for MM38 Exocet missiles were fitted between the funnels. Catapults for L5 anti-submarine torpedoes are fitted immediately below the hangar. *Duperré* has a SENIT 2 action information system which enables her to serve as a command ship. She ran aground in 1978 and was badly damaged, but was subsequently repaired and recommissioned into the Atlantic Squadron in 1980. She is scheduled for disposal at the end of 1985.

Above: *Guépratte* at speed. The success of the original Surcouf (T47) design is illustrated by the long service life of these ships, which are now nearly 30 years old. They have formed the backbone of the French destroyer force over this period.

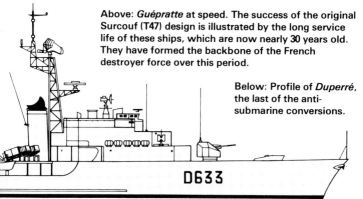

Below: Profile of *Duperré*, the last of the anti-submarine conversions.

D633

Du Chayla class

Completed: 1956–57.
Names: D 625 *Dupetit-Thouars*; D 630 *Du Chayla*.
Displacement: 2,750 tons standard; 3,850 tons full load.
Dimensions: Length 422ft (128.5m) oa; beam 42ft (12.7m); draught 20ft 9in (6.3m) max.
Propulsion: 2-shaft Rateau geared steam turbines; 63,000shp = 32kt.
Weapons: *AAW*: 1 single Mk 13 launcher for Standard SM-1 MR (40 missiles); 6 57mm (3 × 2) AA.
ASW: 1 6-barrelled 375mm launcher; 2 triple tubes for L3 torpedoes.
Sensors: *Surveillance*: SPS-39B, DRBV-22A.
Fire control: SPG-51B (2), DRBC-31.
Sonars: DUBV-24, DUBA-1.
Complement: 275.

These two ships were originally completed as conventional gun-armed fleet escorts of the Surcouf class but underwent a conversion to carry the US Tartar missile system in the early 1960s.

Conversion involved the replacement of the after pair of 5in (127mm) gun mountings by a Mk 13 launcher and magazine, and replacement of the forward 5in mounting by a six-barrelled 375mm Bofors rocket launcher. The original twin 57mm AA mountings were retained, as were the forward banks of torpedo tubes, but the longer torpedo tubes originally fitted aft for surface engagement were suppressed in order to accommodate a new deckhouse atop which the twin SPG-51 tracker/illuminators were located. New lattice masts were fitted, and the radar installation was modified to include a US-model SPS-39A 3-D target designation radar.

From 1968 onwards they were updated: an SPS-39B radar replaced the "A" model, and a SENIT 2 action information system was installed in the after end of

Above: *Du Chayla* in **1984**. Note the long deckhouse aft on which the Tartar surface-to-air missile system is located.

the bridge structure. During the 1970s the Tartar missile was superseded by the Standard SM-1 MR. In 1979 both ships had their original DRBV-20 air surveillance radar replaced by a DRBV-22A.

Two sister-ships *Bouvet* and *Kersaint*, decommissioned in January 1982 and December 1983 respectively to provide missile systems for the first two units of the Cassard class (qv). *Dupetit-Thouars* is due to decommission in 1987, with *Du Chayla* following in 1988. Their Mk 13 launchers will equip the third and fourth units of the Cassard class.

Below: *Dupetit-Thouars* in **1983**. She retains her original 57mm AA guns and anti-submarine torpedo tubes. Both surviving ships of this sub-group have received numerous updates to their electronics, including an SPS-39B planar radar in place of the original SPS-39, and replacement of the DRBV-20 air search radar by a DRBV-22A.

Lütjens class

Completed:	1969–70.
Names:	D 185 *Lütjens*; D 186 *Mölders*; D 187 *Rommel*.
Displacement:	3,370 tons standard; 4,544 tons full load.
Dimensions:	Length 441ft (134.4m) oa; beam 47ft 3in (14.4m); draught 21ft (6.4m) max.
Propulsion:	2-shaft General Electric geared steam turbines; 70,000shp = 35kt.
Weapons:	*AAW*: 1 single launcher Mk 13 for Standard SM-1 MR (40 missiles).
	ASuW: Harpoon missiles from Mk 13 launcher; 2 5in (127mm, 2 × 1) Mk 42 DP.
	ASW: 1 8-cell launcher Mk 16 for ASROC; 2 triple Mk 32 tubes for Mk 44/46 torpedoes.
Sensors:	*Surveillance*: SPS-52, SPS-40, SPS-10.
	Fire control: SPG-51C (2), SPG-60, SPQ-9.
	Sonars: SQS-23.
Complement:	340.

These ships, like the Australian Perth class, are based on the US Navy's Charles F. Adams design. Initially it was envisaged that six units would be built in German shipyards, but in the event it was decided to place orders for only three in the United States. A joint US/German agreement was duly signed in May 1964, and the ships were ordered in April 1965.

The German vessels are fitted with weapons and sensors identical to those of the later US Navy ships; they have the Mk 13 launcher, SPS-52 3-D and SPS-40 air surveillance radars, and an SQS-23 bow sonar. However, there are a number of important differences in the profile of the two types, the German units having modified funnels, with exhausts projecting from the sides, and a tall pole mainmast atop a second funnel.

From 1981 onwards all three ships were updated to fire the Standard SM-1 MR missile in place of Tartar, and they are currently undergoing a modernisation pro-

Above: *Mölders,* the second of the class. Note the projecting funnel exhausts, which serve to distinguish these ships from their US counterparts of the Charles F. Adams class.

gramme similar to that originally proposed for the US Navy ships. A Mk 86 gun fire control system with SPQ-9 and SPQ-60 radars is being fitted, together with the SYS-1 computerised data system, four Mk 36 Super RBOC chaff launchers, and the indigenous FL-1800 electronic countermeasures system. *Mölders* was refitted in 1982–84 and *Rommel* in 1983–85, whilst work on *Lütjens* was scheduled to begin in April 1985. It is planned to modify the Mk 13 launchers and magazine to fire the Harpoon anti-ship missile in 1986–87.

Below: *Lütjens,* the name-ship of the class. These ships have similar weapons and radars to the later units of the Charles F. Adams class. They are currently being fitted with the digital Mk 86 GFCS.

Hamburg class .

Completed:	1964–68.
Names:	D 181 *Hamburg*; D 182 *Schleswig-Holstein*; D 183 *Bayern*; D 184 *Hessen*.
Displacement:	3,500 tons standard; 4,700 tons full load.
Dimensions:	Length 439ft (133.7m) oa; beam 44ft (13.4m); draught 17ft (5.2m) max.
Propulsion:	2-shaft Wahodag geared steam turbines; 72,000shp = 35kt.
Weapons:	*AAW*: 3 3.9in (100mm, 3 × 1) DP; 8 40mm (4 × 2) AA.
	ASuW: 4 MM38 Exocet missiles.
	ASW: 2 4-barrelled 375mm rocket launchers; 4 21in (533mm, 4 × 1) torpedo tubes; 2 depth charge racks.
Sensors:	*Surveillance*: DA-08, LW-04, SRG-103.
	Fire control: M-45 (3).
	Sonars: Atlas ELAC 1BV.
Complement:	280.

Below: *Schleswig-Holstein* in **1980**, when she was a member of the NATO Standing Naval Force Atlantic (STANAVFORLANT). These ships have relatively low freeboard and high, voluminous superstructures. In this view the forward 100mm dual-purpose gun and the 4-barrelled 375mm Bofors ASW rocket launchers are trained to starboard.

Above: The four ships of the Hamburg class are the largest combatants to be built in West German shipyards since World War II.

These were the first destroyers to be built in the Federal Republic after World War II. Germany was prohibited by Treaty from building ships of more than 3,000 tons, and initial plans called for the construction of twelve ships each with a displacement of 2,500 tons. Orders were duly placed in 1957, but it proved impossible to design ships with the required capabilities on the displacement, and shortly afterwards the West European Union permitted an increase in the maximum displacement to 6,000 tons. Following substantial redesign four destroyers of 3,340 tons were ordered; they became the Hamburg class (German Type 101).

The design was essentially conservative. Although the first ship, *Hamburg,* was completed only in 1964, the main armament comprised merely guns, torpedoes and anti-submarine rocket launchers; other European navies, notably the British and French, had already commissioned ships employing guided missiles both for air defence and for anti-submarine work. Like earlier German war-built torpedo boats, which were designed primarily for operations in the shallow waters of the Baltic, the Hamburgs have a top-heavy appearance, with voluminous superstructures and low freeboard.

As completed the Hamburg class had four single 100mm dual-purpose mountings of French design and manufacture, backed up by four twin 40mm AA mountings, disposed symmetrically fore and aft. There were three fixed 21in (533mm) tubes for anti-ship torpedoes in the bow, and a further two in the stern; two trainable tubes for ASW torpedoes were later added amidships. Two ▶

Below: *Hamburg* as she appeared in the late 1970s. The original radar outfit was updated in the early 1970s, and the third 100mm gun mounting was subsequently replaced by four single launchers for MM38 Exocet anti-ship missiles.

▶ forward-firing four-barrelled 375mm ASW rocket launchers were mounted above "B" gun, and there were mine rails running along both sides of the upper deck from abreast the fore-funnel to the stern. The electronics were almost exclusively of Dutch design and manufacture. The foremast carried a DA-08 medium-range air/surface surveillance radar, and there was a large LW-03 antenna for long-range air search on a lattice mainmast forward of the second funnel. The 100mm dual-purpose mountings were controlled by four HSA M-45 FC radars, disposed symmetrically fore and aft.

In the early 1970s the LW-03 air surveillance radar was replaced by an LW-04 on all four ships, and the small lattice tripod mast originally fitted abaft the second funnel was removed. More extensive modifications followed: between 1974 and 1977 the third 100mm mounting was removed and replaced by four single launchers for MM38 Exocet anti-ship missiles, the twin 40mm AA mountings were replaced by a newer model, the fixed (anti-ship) torpedo tubes were removed, and the number of trainable tubes was increased to four. There are now only three M-45 gun fire control directors. Future modifications planned in-

clude the installation of two multiple launchers for the US RAM (Rolling Airframe Missile) short-range air defence system, and a new computer data system.

Although these vessels were initially designed for Baltic operations, their large size makes them suitable for operations in the North Sea and beyond. The expansion of West Germany's maritime role in the NATO Alliance has therefore resulted in frequent deployments with the NATO Standing Naval Force Atlantic STANAVFORLANT).

Below: *Schleswig-Holstein* **in Northern waters during a NATO exercise. Although originally designed primarily for operations in the Baltic, these ships now serve almost exclusively in the North Sea, with frequent deployments to the North Atlantic and the Norwegian Sea. Since the early 1970s they have been fitted with modern radars of Dutch origin. The foremast carries a DA-08 air/surface search radar, and there is an LW-04 air surveillance antenna atop the mainmast. Three M-45 radars have been retained for gun fire control.**

Rajput class

Completed:	1980 onwards.
Names:	D 51 *Rajput*; D 52 *Rana*; D 53 *Ranjit*.
Displacement:	3,950 tons standard; 4,950 tons full load.
Dimensions:	Length 483ft (147m) oa; beam 52ft (15.8m); draught 16ft 6in (5m).
Propulsion:	2-shaft COGAG; 4 gas turbines each of 24,000hp; 96,000hp = 35kt.
Weapons:	*AAW*: 2 twin SA-N-1 launchers (44 Goa missiles); 2 3in (76mm, 1 × 2) DP; 8 30mm (4 × 2) AA.
	ASuW: 4 single launchers for SS-N-2C missiles.
	ASW: 1 Ka-25 Hormone-A helicopter; 2 12-barrelled RBU 6000 rocket launchers; 5 21in (533mm, 1 × 5) torpedo tubes.
Sensors:	*Surveillance*: Big Net, Head Net-C.
	Fire control: Peel Group (2), Owl Screech, Drum Tilt (2).
	Sonars: 1 hull-mounted MF, 1 MF VDS.
Complement:	365.

These vessels are Soviet Kashin derivatives ordered as new construction by India. The first three ships were ordered in the late 1970s, and orders for three more were placed in December 1982. In overall capabilities they resemble the Soviet Kashin-Mod variant (qv), but there are a number of important differences. The four SS-N-2C missile launchers are located abreast the forward superstructure, while a hangar for a single Ka-25 Hormone ASW helicopter, served by an inclined elevator/ramp, has replaced the after 76mm gun mounting. Whereas the Soviet conversions have 30mm Gatlings and Bass Tilt fire control radars in place of the original RBU 1000 anti-submarine rocket launchers, the

---

Audace class

Completed:	1972–73.
Names:	D 550 *Ardito*; D 551 *Audace*.
Displacement:	3,950 tons standard; 4,560 tons full load.
Dimensions:	Length 448ft (136.6m) oa; beam 47ft (14.4m); draught 15ft (4.6m) max.
Propulsion:	2-shaft geared steam turbines; 73,000shp = 33kt.
Weapons:	*AAW*: 1 single launcher Mk 13 for Standard SM-1 MR (40 missiles); 4 76mm (3in, 4x1) OTO Melara DP.
	ASuW: 2 5in (127mm, 2 × 1) OTO Melara DP.
	ASW: 2 AB.212 helicopters or 1 Sea King SH-3D; 4 21in (533mm, 4 × 1), tubes for A-184 torpedoes; 2 triple ILAS-3 tubes for Mk 44/46 torpedoes.
Sensors:	*Surveillance*: RAN-20S, SPQ-2, SPS-52.
	Fire control: SPG-51B (2), RTN-10X Argo (3).
	Sonars: CWE-610.
Complement:	380.

Ordered in the late 1960s, these two ships were derived from the Impavido class but incorporated a number of important advances. A larger, more seaworthy hull with higher freeboard was adopted, and with the exception of the US Standard missile system, the Mk 44/46 anti-submarine torpedoes and the Dutch CWE-610 hull sonar, the weapons and electronics are of Italian design and manufacture.

The gun armament is exceptionally heavy for ships of this size. There are two single 127mm/54 OTO Melara lightweight mountings forward, backed up by four single 76mm/62 OTO Melara Compact mountings amidships. Whereas the Impavido class had facilities only for landing and refuelling an anti-submarine

Above: An unidentified destroyer of the Rajput class. These ships differ from their Soviet counterparts in having their SS-N-2C missile launchers abreast the bridge structure. They are also fitted with a hangar and flight deck for a Ka-25 Hormone-A ASW helicopter. The hangar floor is at upper deck level and doubles as a lift. It now appears that this class will eventually total nine ships.

Indian vessels have the older twin 30mm model, which has a strictly limited anti-missile capability, and Drum Tilt radars.

Above: An early view of *Audace,* with a US-model SPS-12 air search radar atop the forward "mack". The single-arm Mk 13 launcher for Standard SM-1 missiles is visible atop the hangar, which can accommodate two AB.212 anti-submarine helicopters.

helicopter, full maintenance facilities are provided on the Audaces in the form of a broad hangar able to accommodate either two AB.212ASW helicopters or a single SH-3D Sea King. In addition to the triple 12.75in (324mm) torpedo tubes amidships, there are four fixed 21in (533mm) tubes located in the stern. These ▶

▶ fire an Italian Whitehead A-184, a wire-guided torpedo carrier with a range of some 15,000m which ejects a Mk 46 ASW torpedo at the end of its run-out. The ECM equipment, which includes two SCLAR multiple chaff launchers, is exclusively of Italian origin.

As a temporary measure, *Audace* was fitted with a US SPS-12 air surveillance radar on completion while *Ardito,* which entered service a year later, received an Italian RAN-3 model. Both ships have since been fitted with the advanced RAN-20S radar, which has superior long-range performance. There is an Italian SPQ-2 radar for surface search, and gun fire control is provided by the Argo NA 10 system, which employs three lightweight RTN-10X radars.

The Audace class has proved very successful in service, and during the late 1970s two further ships of a modified design were approved as replacements for the old gun-armed destroyers of the Impetuoso class. The design has undergone numerous changes since its conception. It is now envisaged that these two vessels, provisionally named *Animoso* and *Ardimento*, will have CODOG propulsion machinery employing two uprated LM 2500 gas turbines for boost, with GMT B230 diesels for cruising. Two SH-3D Sea King ASW helicopters will be carried, and there will be four 76mm/62 OTO Melara Compact guns and three twin Breda-Bofors 40mm mountings to complement the single Mk 13 launcher. The armament will be completed by triple ILAS-3 torpedo tubes and four single launchers for Teseo anti-ship missiles.

Financial problems have delayed the construction of these ships, and they have yet to be authorised.

Above: A recent view of *Audace,* with the barrels of her forward 127mm dual-purpose guns and midships OTO 76mm Compact guns elevated.

Below: *Ardito* and her sister *Audace* now have the Italian RAN-20S air surveillance radar in place of the earlier models initially fitted.

Impavido class

Completed: 1963–64.
Names: D 570 *Impavido*; D 571 *Intrepido*.
Displacement: 3,200 tons standard; 3,990 tons full load.
Dimensions: Length 431ft (131.3m) oa; beam 45ft (13.7m); draught 14ft 6in (4.4m).
Propulsion: 2-shaft Tosi geared steam turbines; 70,000shp = 33.5kt.
Weapons: *AAW*: 1 single launcher Mk 13 for Standard SM-1 MR (40 missiles); 4 76mm (4 x 1) AA.
ASuW: 2 5in (127mm, 1 x 2) DP.
ASW: 2 triple ILAS-3 tubes for Mk 44/46 torpedoes.
Sensors: *Surveillance*: SPS-52B, SPS-12, SPQ-2.
Fire control: SPG-51B (2), RTN-10X Argo (3).
Sonars: SQS-23.
Complement: 334.

Derived from the conventional gun-armed destroyers of the Impetuoso class, these two ships were the first Italian destroyers to carry guided missiles. They retained the forward twin 5in/38 gun mounting of their predecessors, but the after 5in mounting was replaced by a US Mk 13 single-arm launcher for Tartar surface-to-air missiles. The funnels had to be heightened to keep corrosive exhaust gases clear of the SPG-51 tracker/illuminators mounted atop the after deckhouse. Four single 76mm AA mountings of Italian design and manufacture replaced the numerous 40mm weapons of the Impetuoso class, and a more advanced electronics outfit was installed. The only anti-submarine weapons are Mk 44/46 torpedoes, fired from two triple ILAS-3 tubes located at 01 level abreast the forward superstructure. Provision was made for landing and refuelling an AB.204B ASW helicopter on the quarterdeck, but there are no fixed maintenance facilities.

As completed, the ships were fitted almost exclusively with weapons and sen-

Left: The guided missile destroyer *Intrepido*. The large twin 5in/38 gun mounting forward is the standard US dual-purpose mounting of the Second World War. The influence of the US Navy can also be seen in the flush-deck hull configuration, the tall, raked funnels, and the electronics outfit. More recent Italian destroyers have guns and radars of indigenous design and manufacture.

sors of US origin, but later modifications have included the fitting of an Italian Argo gun fire control system employing three RTN-10X radars. One is fitted atop the bridge, while the other two are located port and starboard atop a tall deckhouse between the lattice mainmast and the second funnel. *Intrepido* was modernised in 1974–75, with *Impavido* following in 1976–77. They can now fire the Standard SM-1 MR missile, which has replaced Tartar, and the original SPS-39 antenna has been replaced by an SPA-72 planar antenna. They are now comparable with the destroyers of the Audace class as regards their defence capabilities.

Below: *Impavido* at sea in the Mediterranean. The anti-submarine helicopter on the stern is an Agusta-Bell AB.212. Facilities for landing and refuelling a helicopter are provided, but there is no hangar, nor is there any provision for maintenance of the machine.

Shirane class

Completed:	1980–81.
Names:	DDH 143 *Shirane*; DDH 144 *Kurama*.
Displacement:	5,200 tons standard; 6,800 tons full load.
Dimensions:	Length 521ft (158.8m) pp; beam 57ft 6in (17.5m); draught 17ft 6in (5.3m) max.
Propulsion:	2-shaft geared steam turbines; 70,000shp = 32kt.
Weapons:	*AAW*: 1 8-cell launcher Mk 25 for Sea Sparrow; 2 20mm Phalanx CIWS.
	ASuW: 2 5in (127mm, 2 x 1) Mk 42 DP.
	ASW: 3 Sea King HSS-2B helicopters; 1 8-cell launcher Mk 16 for ASROC; 2 triple Mk 68 tubes for Mk 46 torpedoes.
Sensors:	*Surveillance*: OPS-12, OPS-28.
	Fire control: WM-25, GFCS-1A (2).
	Sonars: OQS-101, SQS-35(J) VDS, SQR-18A TACTAS.
Complement:	370.

These two ships are improved Harunas (qv), with enhanced air defence capabilities and more advanced electronics. They can be distinguished externally from their predecessors by their distinctive twin funnels. The helicopter arrangements are essentially the same, but the large hangar for the three HSS-2B Sea King helicopters extends to port of the boiler uptakes for the second funnel.

Above: *Kurama,* **The latest of Japan's large helicopter-carrying destroyers (DDH). She differs from her sister** *Shirane* **primarily in being fitted with two Vulcan/Phalanx 20mm CIWS guns, which are located on platforms between the funnels. The guns and air defence missiles are of American origin, but the air surveillance and gun fire control radars are of Japanese design and manufacture.**

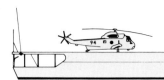

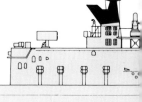

Above: *Shirane* underway in the north-west Pacific. Three large HSS-2B Sea King anti-submarine helicopters can be accommodated in the large hangar, which occupies the full beam of the ships. The second funnel is offset to starboard to create sufficient hangar space for the third helicopter. Note the SATCOMM radomes abreast the forefunnel.

The 5in/54 Mk 42 gun mountings, the ASROC missile launcher and the triple anti-submarine torpedo tubes are located in identical fashion to those of the Harunas, but there is in addition an eight-cell launcher for Sea Sparrow surface-to-air missiles mounted atop the hangar. Long-range air surveillance and target designation for the missiles are provided by an OPS-12 3-D planar radar of Japanese design and manufacture, and fire control by a Dutch WM-25, mounted atop the second funnel. *Kurama*, the second ship, was also fitted with two Vulcan/Phalanx 20mm CIWS guns on completion, and these will eventually be retrofitted to her sister. Harpoon anti-ship missiles will also be installed at further refits.

These ships have a more advanced and more comprehensive sonar outfit than the Harunas. The hull sonar is the latest OQS-101 low-frequency model, similar in capabilities to the US Navy's SQS-26/53 series. Both ships were fitted from the outset with an SQS-35(J) variable-depth sonar, and in 1981 they received the US SQR-18A TACTAS towed array, which is streamed from the SQS-35 "fish".

Shirane and *Kurama* have advanced data processing and display systems, and LINK 11 and LINK 14 tactical data links. They serve as command ships for ASW escort groups each comprising one or two 3-ship divisions of modern anti-submarine destroyers and a two-ship division of air defence destroyers.

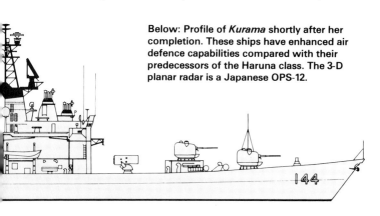

Below: Profile of *Kurama* shortly after her completion. These ships have enhanced air defence capabilities compared with their predecessors of the Haruna class. The 3-D planar radar is a Japanese OPS-12.

JAPAN

Haruna class

Completed:	1973–74.
Names:	DDH 141 *Haruna*; DDH 142 *Hiei*.
Displacement:	4,700 tons standard; 6,300 tons full load.
Dimensions:	Length 502ft (153m) pp; beam 57ft 6in (17.5m); draught 16ft 9in (5.1m) max.
Propulsion:	2-shaft geared steam turbines; 70,000shp = 32kt.
Weapons:	*ASuW*: 2 5in (127mm, 2 x 1) Mk 42 DP.
	ASW: 3 Sea King HSS-2B helicopters; 1 8-cell launcher Mk 16 for ASROC; 2 triple Mk 32 tubes for Mk 44/46 torpedoes.
Sensors:	*Surveillance*: OPS-11, OPS-17.
	Fire control: GFCS-1 (2).
	Sonars: OQS-3.
Complement:	340.

These two unusual vessels were designed in the late 1960s. The entire after part of the ship is dedicated to operating facilities for three large HSS-2B Sea King anti-submarine helicopters. The midships section is dominated by the hangar, which occupies the full beam of the ship and extends forward alongside the single broad funnel, which is offset to port. The hangar exits on to a broad flight deck on which is marked out a single landing spot. A Canadian Beartrap haul-down system is employed for securing the Sea King helicopters, and there is a large aircraft-handling crane located atop the after end of the hangar. Fin stabilisers are fitted to enable the ships to maintain helicopter operations in hostile weather conditions.

For medium/close-range anti-submarine work there is an ASROC launcher forward of the bridge structure and triple Mk 32 torpedo tubes amidships. The only air defence weapons initially fitted were the two 5in/54 Mk 42 guns located on the forecastle, controlled by two Japanese Mk 1A gun fire control radars. This deficiency is now being remedied by the installation of an eight-cell launcher

Above: The helicopter destroyer *Hiei*. One of her three HSS-2B Sea Kings is parked on the flight deck. *Hiei* and her sister *Haruna* are large, spacious vessels with well-designed helicopter facilities.

for NATO Sea Sparrow missiles, two Vulcan/Phalanx 20mm CIWS guns, and a new electronic countermeasures outfit. Funds for the modernisation of *Haruna* were authorised under the 1983 budget, and the refit is due for completion in 1987. In addition to the enhancement of her air defence capabilities, she will receive Harpoon anti-ship missiles and an SQS-35(J) variable-depth sonar (for which provision was made in the original design). Her sister *Hiei* will undergo similar modifications in the late 1980s.

Like the Shirane class, these two units are employed as command ships for ASW escort groups each comprising two 2/3-ship divisions of anti-submarine destroyers. *Haruna* and *Hiei* currently operate with the destroyers of the Takatsuki and Yamagumo classes.

Left: *Haruna* under full helm. Stabilisers contribute to a very steady helicopter platform. The major weakness of these ships is their lack of effective air defence and anti-missile systems. This will be remedied during their current refit.

Below: *Haruna* and *Hiei* each serve as the flagship of an anti-submarine escort group made up of two 2/3-ship divisions of ASW destroyers. These groups operate in defence of the shipping lanes around Japan, which are threatened by the Soviet Pacific Fleet.

Hatakaze class

Completed:	1988 onwards.
Names:	DDG 171 *Hatakaze*; DDG 172.
Displacement:	4,450 tons standard; 5,400 tons full load.
Dimensions:	Length 492ft (150m) pp; beam 54ft (16.4m); draught 15ft 9in (4.8m).
Propulsion:	2-shaft COGAG; 2 Olympus TM3D gas turbines, 2 Spey SM1A gas turbines; 90,000hp = 32kt.
Weapons:	*AAW*: 1 single launcher Mk 13 for Standard SM-1 MR (40 missiles); 2 20mm Phalanx CIWS.
	ASuW: 2 quadruple launchers for Harpoon missiles; 2 5in (127mm, 2 x 1) Mk 42 DP.
	ASW: 1 8-cell launcher Mk 16 for ASROC; 2 triple Mk 68 tubes for Mk 46 torpedoes.

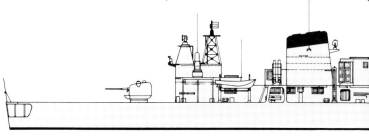

Tachikaze class

Completed:	1976–83.
Names:	DDG 168 *Tachikaze*; DDG 169 *Asakaze*; DDG 170 *Sawakaze*.
Displacement:	3,850 tons standard; 4,800 tons full load.
Dimensions:	Length 469ft (143m) pp; beam 46ft 9in (14.3m); draught 15ft (4.6m) max.
Propulsion:	2-shaft geared steam turbines; 70,000shp = 32kt.
Weapons:	*AAW*: 1 single Mk 13 launcher for Standard SM-1 MR (40 missiles).
	ASuW: 2 5in (127mm, 2 x 1) Mk 42 DP.
	ASW: 1 8-cell launcher Mk 16 for ASROC; 2 triple Mk 32 tubes for Mk 44/46 torpedoes.
Sensors:	*Surveillance*: SPS-52B, OPS-11, OPS-17 (OPS-28 in *Sawakaze*).
	Fire control: SPG-51C (2), GFCS-1 (GFCS-2 in *Sawakaze*).
	Sonars: OQS-3 (OQS-4 in *Sawakaze)*.
Complement:	277.

The three ships of the Tachikaze class are larger, improved versions of *Amatsukaze*. Whereas the latter ship mounted twin 3in/50 guns forward, the Tachikazes have the more powerful 5in/54 Mk 42, and the two single mountings are distributed fore and aft, thereby freeing ''B'' position for the ASROC launcher, which can fire on forward bearings. The tall twin ''macks'' are reminiscent of the US Navy's missile ''frigates'' (now cruisers) of the Leahy and Belknap classes.

The electronics of *Amatsukaze* were exlusively of US origin; but the systems installed in *Tachikaze* are largely of Japanese manufacture and some, including the Mk 1 gun fire control system and the OPS-11 radar, are of Japanese design.

The three ships of the class have been completed at intervals of 3–4 years. It is ▶

Sensors: *Surveillance*: OPS-12, OPS-11, OPS-28.
          Fire control: SPG-51C (2), GFCS-2.
          Sonars: OQS-4.

Complement: ?

The Hatakaze class is a development of the Tachikaze class, but with an all-gas-turbine propulsion plant replacing the steam machinery of the earlier ships. The adoption of gas turbines has led to some rearrangement of the major weapons systems, and in particular the location of the Mk 13 missile launcher on the forecastle with the associated SPG-51 tracker/illuminators above the bridge, well forward of the hot exhaust gases emanating from the single funnel. Improvements over the Tachikazes include more advanced electronics, a comprehensive outfit of anti-missile systems including two Phalanx CIWS guns and Super RBOC chaff launchers, and quadruple launchers for Harpoon anti-ship missiles.

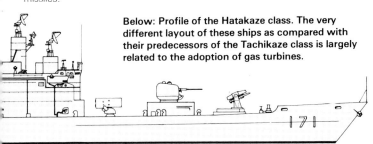

Below: Profile of the Hatakaze class. The very different layout of these ships as compared with their predecessors of the Tachikaze class is largely related to the adoption of gas turbines.

Above: *Sawakaze,* the third unit of the Tachikaze class. She incorporates a number of improvements, including an OPS-28 surface search radar (atop the foremast) in place of the US-derived OPS-17 of the earlier ships, a Japanese Mk 2 digital gun fire control system, an OQS-4 sonar in place of the OQS-3, and a reload magazine in the bridge face for the ASROC launcher. US influence on the design is apparent.

▶ therefore not surprising that the two later vessels have incorporated a number of improvements, some of which are being retrofitted to *Tachikaze*. *Asakaze*, which entered service in 1979, introduced a new electronic countermeasures outfit and was the first ship of the class to be fitted with the Japanese OPS-11 air surveillance radar on completion. *Sawakaze*, which was completed only in 1983, has a Japanese OPS-28 surface surveillance radar in place of the US-derived OPS-17 of the earlier two vessels. She also has the new OQS-4 hull sonar, the digital Mk 2 gun fire control system, and a reload magazine for ASROC (located beneath the forward part of the bridge structure). *Sawakaze* can be further distinguished from her sisters by the constant-tension solid stores transfer stations located between the funnels.

Tachikaze has now been fitted with the OPS-11 air surveillance radar, and funds for two Phalanx CIWS guns have been approved. All three ships are currently being fitted for satellite communications.

Below: *Asakaze*, with the Japanese Mk 1 GFCS. She was the first of the class to receive the OPS-11 air surveillance radar on completion.

JAPAN

Amatsukaze class

Completed:	1965.
Names:	DDG 163 *Amatsukaze*.
Displacement:	3,050 tons standard; 4,000 tons full load.
Dimensions:	Length 430ft (131m) pp; beam 44ft (13.4m); draught 13ft 9in (4.2m).
Propulsion:	2-shaft Ishikawajima-GE geared steam turbines; 60,000shp = 33kt.
Weapons:	*AAW*: 1 single Mk 13 launcher for Standard SM-1 MR (40 missiles); 4 3in (76mm, 2 × 2) Mk 33 DP.
	ASW: 1 8-cell launcher Mk 16 for ASROC; 2 triple Mk 32

Right: *Amatsukaze*, the first of Japan's air defence missile destroyers. Her weapons systems and radars, unlike those of later vessels, are exclusively of US origin. Note the SPG-34 radars mounted on the face of the twin 3in gun mountings, and the Mk 63 gun director beneath a perspex radome atop the bridge structure. The latter has recently been replaced by a Japanese Mk 2 fire control system. Between the gun mountings are Mk 15 trainable Hedgehog anti-submarine mortars. The ASROC launcher is between the funnels, as in the US Navy's Charles F. Adams class. Italian-designed 76mm guns may in due course be fitted to this ship.

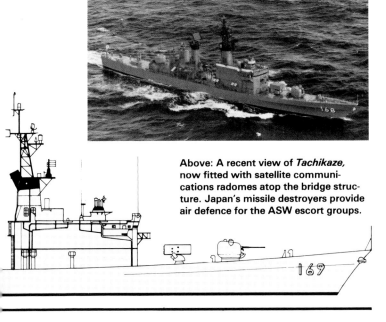

Above: A recent view of *Tachikaze*, now fitted with satellite communications radomes atop the bridge structure. Japan's missile destroyers provide air defence for the ASW escort groups.

	tubes for Mk 44/46 torpedoes; 2 Mk 15 trainable Hedgehog.
Sensors:	*Surveillance*: SPS-52, SPS-29, OPS-17.
	Fire control: SPG-51 (2), GFCS-2.
	Sonars: SQS-23.
Complement:	290.

Japan's first guided-missile destroyer was built in the remarkably short period of 27 months. The weapon/sensor outfit closely resembles that of the US Navy's Charles F. Adams class, but twin 3in/50 mountings were preferred to the single 5in Mk 42 mountings of the latter, and the style of the ship's architecture is unmistakably Japanese. A Japanese gun fire control system Mk 2 was fitted in place of the former US Mk 63 in the early 1980s, and the ECM outfit was updated. A proposal to replace the 3in guns with single 76mm OTO Melara Compact mountings has not yet been authorised.

Hatsuyuki class

Completed:	1982 onwards.
Names:	DD 122 *Hatsuyuki*; DD 123 *Shirayuki*; DD 124 *Mineyuki*; DD 125 *Sawayuki*; DD 126 *Hamayuki*; DD 127 *Isoyuki*; DD 128 *Haruyuki*; DD 129 *Yamayuki*; DD 130 *Matsuyuki*; DD 131–133 (building).
Displacement:	2,950 tons standard; 3,700 tons full load.
Dimensions:	Length 432ft (131.7m) oa; beam 45ft (13.7m); draught 14ft 3in (4.3m) max.
Propulsion:	2-shaft COGOG; 2 Kawasaki-RR Olympus TM3B gas turbines, 56,780hp = 30kt; 2 Tyne RM1C gas turbines, 10,680hp.
Weapons:	*AAW*: 1 8-cell launcher Mk 25 for NATO Sea Sparrow; 1 3in (76mm) OTO Melara DP; 2 20mm Phalanx CIWS in *Mineyuki* onwards. *ASuW*: 2 quadruple launchers for Harpoon. *ASW*: 1 Sea King HSS-2B helicopter; 1 8-cell launcher Mk 16 for ASROC; 2 triple Mk 68 tubes for Mk 46 torpedoes.
Sensors:	*Surveillance*: OPS-14B, OPS-18. *Fire control*: MFCS-2, GFCS-2. *Sonars*: OQS-4.
Complement:	190.

Above: *Hamayuki,* the first of the class to
incorporate the new anti-missile systems: two
Phalanx 20mm CIWS guns atop the bridge structure
and Super RBOC chaff launchers atop the hangar.

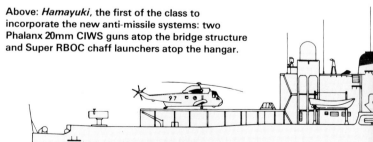

Above: *Hatsuyuki*, the name-ship of a new 12-ship class of Japanese anti-submarine destroyers. Note the sloping hangar roof, which has been modified in other ships of the class.

The anti-submarine destroyers of the Hatsuyuki class represent a completely new design, owing little to the earlier Japanese ASW destroyers of the Takatsuki and Yamagumo classes. Whilst the weapons carried remain largely of US origin, in concept and general layout the ships closely resemble the French ASW *corvettes* of the Georges Leygues class. The similarities extend to the single broad funnel, which houses all four uptakes for the British COGOG propulsion machinery, and the tall lattice foremast which carries the major above-water sensors. The Rolls-Royce Olympus/Tyne combination was apparently selected because of the greater fuel economy offered by separate cruise turbines in ships of this size.

The HSS-2B Sea King helicopter, already operational with the JMSDF from the two DDHs of the Haruna class, was preferred to the smaller models available. The size of the Sea King has led the Japanese to adopt similar operating arrangements to those favoured by the US Navy and the Canadian Navy, with the flight deck at 01 level and the hangar amidships. The formidable operating radius of the Sea King is complemented by the standard medium/short-range ASW weapons in service with the JMSDF, and there is an OQS-4 low-frequency hull sonar of Japanese design and manufacture. All ships of the class are scheduled to receive the US SQR-19 TACTAS towed array at future refits. ▶

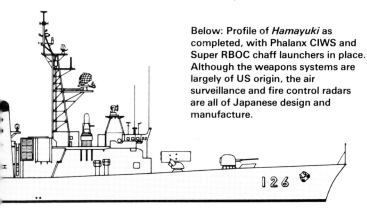

Below: Profile of *Hamayuki* as completed, with Phalanx CIWS and Super RBOC chaff launchers in place. Although the weapons systems are largely of US origin, the air surveillance and fire control radars are all of Japanese design and manufacture.

More attention has been paid to air defence than in earlier Japanese ASW destroyers. A Mk 29 launcher for NATO Sea Sparrow missiles is fitted on the stern, while forward arcs are covered by a 76mm OTO Melara Compact gun mounted on the forecastle. Fire control for both systems is provided by the latest MFCS-2 and GFCS-2 radars, and there is a medium-range OPS-14 radar of Japanese design and manufacture to provide initial detection of hostile air targets. The second ship of the class, *Shirayuki,* has provision for the installation of two Phalanx CIWS guns and Mk 36 Super RBOC chaff launchers, and all subsequent ships have been completed with these two systems in place. Harpoon missiles have superseded the 5in Mk 42 mountings of the Takatsuki class in the anti-ship role.

The Hatsuyuki class represent a major part of the current building programme of the JMSDF, with twelve units completed or under construction. They will be superseded by a modified design known as the Improved Hatsuyuki. The order for the first of the new series was placed in March 1984, and six additional units have since been authorised.

The major difference between the Improved Hatsuyuki and the original design lies in the propulsion system. In place of the Olympus/Tyne combination there will be a COGAG arrangement employing four Rolls-Royce Spey SM1A gas turbines, each with a rating of 17,100hp. The Speys will be paired in a unit arrangement, with the funnels *en echelon* as in the US Navy's Spruance class. This has made it possible to accommodate a second lattice mast abreast the second funnel, and the additional space created between the funnels has been utilised to

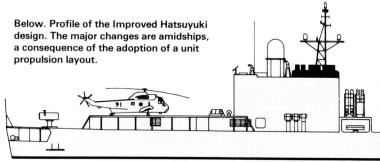

Below. Profile of the Improved Hatsuyuki design. The major changes are amidships, a consequence of the adoption of a unit propulsion layout.

Above: The recently completed *Mineyuki*, with Phalanx guns and Super RBOC chaff launchers. The GRP radome atop the hangar houses the MFCS-2 missile fire control radar for NATO Sea Sparrow. Note the broad flight deck on 01 level for the single HSS-2B Sea King.

Left: *Shirayuki*, the second ship of the class. She has provision for the installation of Phalanx CIWS guns and Super RBOC chaff launchers, but has yet to receive either system.

provide a more satisfactory layout for the Harpoon launchers, which are located on a shelter deck occupying the full beam of the ship with the triple Mk 68 torpedo tubes beneath. The layout of the forward and after parts of the ship is similar to that of the Hatsuyukis, and the weapons outfit of the two sub-groups is identical. However, the Improved Hatsuyukis will incorporate a number of improvements in electronics, including the replacement of the OPS-18 surface search radar by the OPS-28 and a more comprehensive ECM outfit.

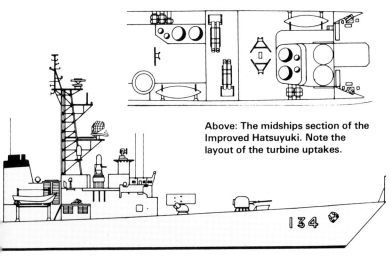

Above: The midships section of the Improved Hatsuyuki. Note the layout of the turbine uptakes.

Takatsuki class

Completed:	1967–70.
Names:	DD 164 *Takatsuki*; DD 165 *Kikuzuki*; DD 166 *Mochizuki*; DD 167 *Nagatsuki*.
Displacement:	3,200 tons standard; 4,500 tons full load.
Dimensions:	Length 446ft (136m) oa; beam 44ft (13.4m); draught 14ft 6in (4.4m).
Propulsion:	2-shaft Mitsubishi geared steam turbines; 60,000shp = 32kt.
Weapons:	*AAW*: 1 8-cell launcher Mk 29 for NATO Sea Sparrow (DD 164 only).
	ASuW: 2 quadruple launchers for Harpoon (DD 164 only); 1 5in (127mm) Mk 42 DP in DD 164; 2 5in (127mm, 2 × 1) Mk 42 in others.
	ASW: 1 8-cell launcher Mk 16 for ASROC; 1 4-barrelled 375mm rocket launcher; 2 triple Mk 32 tubes for Mk 44/46 torpedoes.
Sensors:	*Surveillance*: OPS-11, OPS-17.
	Fire control: MFCS-2, SPG-35 in DD 164; SPG-35 (2) in others.
	Sonars: SQS-23 in DD 164–65; OQS-3 in DD 166–67; SQR-18A TACTAS in DD 164; SQS-35(J) VDS in DD 165, 167.
Complement:	270.

These fleet ASW destroyers are the first-line counterparts of the diesel-powered DDKs of the Yamagumo and Minegumo classes. As completed, they were fitted with a broad hangar aft for three DASH drone anti-submarine helicopters. The particularly comprehensive ASW armament was completed by an ASROC launcher forward of the bridge structure, a quadruple 375mm rocket launcher close to the bow, and triple Mk 32 torpedo tubes amidships. Single 5in/54 Mk 42 gun mountings were fitted forward and aft for air defence and anti-surface work. The sensor outfit was similar to that of the DDKs, but there were US Mk 56 fire control systems forward and aft for the 5in guns.

These ships have proved very successful in service, but although the JMSDF persisted with DASH long after the concept had lost favour with the US Navy, it was decided in the late 1970s to dispense with this capability and a major modernisation of *Takatsuki* was authorised under the 1981–82 budget. The DASH hangar and the after 5in gun mounting will be removed and quadruple launchers for Harpoon anti-ship missiles will be fitted atop a new deckhouse aft. On the former flight deck a Mk 29 launcher for NATO Sea Sparrow missiles will be in-

Above: The anti-submarine destroyer *Nagatsuki*. Her weapons systems are of US origin, but the air search radars are Japanese.

stalled, controlled by an MFCS-2 radar mounted immediately abaft the second funnel. Provision will be made for fitting two Phalanx CIWS mountings atop the after deckhouse. *Takatsuki* will also receive an SQR-18A TACTAS towed array, LINK 14 tactical data link equipment, and a new electronic countermeasures outfit including US Mk 36 Super RBOC chaff launchers.

Takatsuki is due to complete her refit in late 1985 and a second ship, *Kikuzuki*, has now been taken in hand for similar modifications and will complete in late 1988. *Mochizuki* and *Nagatsuki* were due to follow, but it has now been decided to limit the modernisation programme to two ships in order to make more money available for new construction.

Below: *Mochizuki*, the third ship of the class. The small hangar aft was designed to accommodate three DASH anti-submarine drones, and these continued in service with the JMSDF until the late 1970s, when they were finally discarded. In *Takatsuki* and *Kikuzuki* the hangar will be replaced by a deckhouse carrying new weapons systems.

Yamagumo class

Completed:	1966–78.
Names:	DDK 113 *Yamagumo*; DDK 114 *Makigumo*; DDK 115 *Asagumo*; DDK 119 *Aokumo*; DDK 120 *Akigumo*; DDK 121 *Yuugumo*.
Displacement:	2,100 tons standard; 2,700 tons full load.
Dimensions:	Length 377ft (114.9m) pp; beam 38ft 9in (11.8m); draught 13ft (4m) max.
Propulsion:	2-shafts; 6 Mitsubishi 12UEV 30/40 or Mitsui diesels; 26,500bhp = 27kt.
Weapons:	*AAW*: 4 3in (76mm, 2 × 2) Mk 33 DP. *ASW*: 1 8-cell launcher Mk 16 for ASROC; 1 4-barrelled 375mm rocket launcher; 2 triple Mk 32 tubes for Mk 44/46 torpedoes.
Sensors:	*Surveillance*: OPS-11, OPS-17. *Fire control*: SPG-34, SPG-35 in DDK 113–15, 119; GFCS-1(2) in DDK 120–21. *Sonars*: SQS-23 in DDK 113–15; OQS-3 in DDK 119–21; SQS-35(J) in all except DDK 115.
Complement:	210.

These unusual vessels, designated anti-submarine hunter-killer destroyers (DDKs), are an updated version of the destroyer escorts built for the US Navy in the immediate postwar period. They are powered by six diesel engines on two shafts. They are well equipped for ASW operations, with a low-frequency hull sonar, an SQS-35(J) variable-depth sonar, and a full range of short/medium-

---

Minegumo class

Completed:	1968–70.
Names:	DDK 116 *Minegumo*; DDK 117 *Natsugumo*; DDK 118 *Murakumo*.
Displacement:	As Yamagumo class.
Dimensions:	As Yamagumo class.
Propulsion:	As Yamagumo class.
Weapons:	*AAW*: 4 3in (76mm, 2 × 2) Mk 33 DP in DDK 116, 117; 2 3in (76mm, 1 × 2) Mk 33, 1 3in (76mm) OTO Melara DP in DDK 118. *ASW*: 1 8-cell launcher Mk 16 for ASROC; 1 4-barrelled 375mm rocket launcher; 2 triple Mk 32 tubes for Mk 44/46 torpedoes.
Sensors:	*Surveillance*: OPS-11, OPS-17. *Fire control*: SPG-35; SPG-34 in DDK 116, 117, GFCS-2 in DDK 118 *Sonars*: OQS-3; SQS-35(J) in DDK 118 only.
Complement:	215.

The three ships of the Minegumo class have many features in common with the Yamagumo class but were completed with a broad single funnel and a hangar for DASH anti-submarine drones in place of ASROC. DASH is no longer operational with the JMSDF, and in 1976 *Murakumo* underwent a prototype conversion in which an ASROC launcher was fitted on the former flight deck, and the after 3in/50 mounting was replaced by a single 76mm OTO Melara Compact gun controlled by a Japanese gun fire control system Mk 2. It is envisaged that these modifications will be extended to the other two ships, and that the forward 3in/50 mounting will be replaced by a second 76mm Compact gun in all three.

Above: *Aokumo* in company with her sister *Akigumo.* These "hunter-killer" destroyers are unusual in having diesel propulsion. They have a comprehensive outfit of anti-submarine weapons.

range anti-submarine weapons, but they have no helicopters, and carry only twin 3in/50 gun mountings for air defence. There are two sub-groups, each of three ships. Differences include the electronics (especially the gun fire control systems) and the configuration of the mainmast and the stern. The 3in/50 mountings may be replaced by 76mm OTO Melara Compact guns at later refits.

Above: *Murakumo* now has an ASROC launcher in place of the former DASH hangar and an OTO Melara 76mm Compact gun in place of the after twin 3in Mk 33.

Below: *Minegumo* at speed. She and *Natsugumo* retain their DASH hangar although the drone is no longer operational. The air search radar is an OPS-11.

Tromp class

Completed: 1975–76.
Names: F 801 *Tromp*; F 802 *De Ruyter.*
Displacement: 4,300 tons standard; 5,400 tons full load.
Dimensions: Length 453ft (138.2m) oa; beam 49ft (14.8m);
draught 21ft 6in (6.6m) max.
Propulsion: 2-shaft COGOG; 2 Olympus TM3B gas turbines,
44,000hp = 28kt; 2 Tyne RM1A gas turbines, 8,200hp = 18kt.
Weapons: *AAW*: 1 single launcher Mk 13 for Standard SM-1 MR (40
missiles); 1 8-cell launcher Mk 29 for NATO Sea Sparrow (60
missiles).
ASuW: 2 quadruple launchers for Harpoon missiles; 2 4.7in
(120mm, 1 × 2) DP.
ASW: 1 WG.13 Lynx helicopter; 2 triple Mk 32 tubes for Mk
46 torpedoes.
Sensors: *Surveillance*: SPS-01, ZW-05 (2).
Fire control: SPG-51C (2), WM-25.
Sonars: CWE-610, Type 162.
Complement: 305.

These two ships were built as replacements for the cruisers *De Ruyter* and *De Zeven Provincien* to serve as air defence flagships for anti-submarine squadrons each comprising six frigates and a combat support ship operating in the Eastern Atlantic area of the NATO command. Although the Royal Netherlands Navy designates them as "frigates" and they carry "F" pennant numbers, in overall size and mission they compare with the guided-missile destroyers in service with other Western navies.

Above: *Tromp* and her sister *De Ruyter* are classified as "frigates" by the Royal Netherlands Navy, and serve as flagships for two of the three anti-submarine groups allocated to NATO's EASTLANT command. Each group comprises six frigates plus a Combat Support Ship.

Above: *Tromp* shortly after completion, and still without her pennant number. The large radome above the bridge structure houses the HSA SPS-01 3-D radar, which combines the search and tracking functions.

Originally they were to have been fitted with the British Sea Dart missile system in return for an agreement by the Royal Navy to purchase the advanced Dutch "broomstick" radar for the new generation of carriers and for the destroyers of the Type 82 class. In the event, however, Sea Dart proved to be too volume-intensive and too costly, and the US Navy's Tartar system was purchased instead. It is paired with the Dutch SPS-01, a multi-function radar which provides both long-range air surveillance and 3-D tracking capabilities. The SPS-01 is housed beneath a distinctive GRP radome mounted atop the bridge structure. It may be replaced by the HSA SMART 3-D radar currently under development at a future refit.

For close-range air defence a NATO Sea Sparrow system is fitted forward of the bridge. Besides the eight missiles in the Mk 29 launcher there is a reload magazine for a further 52 rounds. The twin 120mm dual-purpose mountings for the two ships were removed from the old destroyer *Gelderland*; the mountings were refurbished and numerous modifications were made, including the provision of full automation. Both the Sea Sparrow missiles and the 120mm mountings are controlled by an HSA WM-25 fire control radar located immediately forward of the bridge. A Dutch SEWACO-1 action information system based on DAISY-1 computers is fitted for data co-ordination and weapons control.

For ASW work there is a single WG.13 Lynx helicopter and triple Mk 32 torpedo tubes, and the excellent all-round qualities of these ships are completed by the installation of Harpoon anti-ship missiles. Only four canisters are normally fitted, but in the event of hostilities eight would be carried.

Originally these ships were to have had steam propulsion machinery, but a British COGOG installation combining Olympus main drive turbines and Tyne ▶

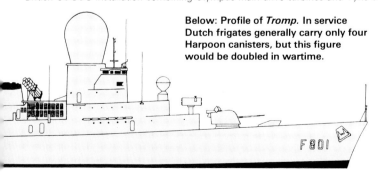

Below: Profile of *Tromp*. In service Dutch frigates generally carry only four Harpoon canisters, but this figure would be doubled in wartime.

F801

cruise turbines was eventually selected to economise on manning. The Netherlands Navy was not entirely happy with the power rating of the Tynes, and it is envisaged that they will be replaced during the ships' half-life refit. All the machinery is flexibly mounted, and the diesel generators are on double-mounting systems with noise-absorbent hoods to reduce the acoustic signature of the vessels. In order to minimise the effects of the hot exhaust gases on electronic equipment, twin canted funnels, similar to those on the Canadian Iroquois class, were adopted.

The combination of high freeboard and a relatively broad hull-form gives the ships excellent sea-keeping qualities for their mission in the inhospitable waters of the North Atlantic, and they have proved very successful in service.

Below: *Tromp* at speed. The twin 120mm gun mounting on the forecastle was removed from the old destroyer *Gelderland*. Two air defence missile systems are fitted: a US Tartar/Standard medium-range area defence system aft and a NATO Sea Sparrow short-range system forward. The Sea Sparrow launcher has a reload magazine for a total of 60 missiles. Both the 120mm mounting and the Sea Sparrow missiles are controlled by the WM-25 radar, housed within the smaller of the two radomes. Anti-submarine capabilities centre on a single WG-13 Lynx helicopter and triple Mk 32 tubes for Mk 46 torpedoes, giving these ships good all-round qualities. High freeboard combined with a broad beam gives them excellent sea-keeping qualities.

Coronel Bolognesi class

Completed:	1954–58.
Names:	70 *Coronel Bolognesi*; 71 *Castilla*; 72 *Guise*; 76 *Capitán Quiñones*; 77 *Villar*; 78 *Galvez*; 79 *Diez Canseco*. Also 75 *García y García*.
Displacement:	(*Bolognesi*) 2,500 tons standard; 3,100 tons full load.
Dimensions:	Length 381ft (116m) oa; beam 38ft (11.7m); draught 17ft (5.2m).
Propulsion:	2-shaft Werkspoor geared steam turbines, 60,000shp = 36kt.
Weapons:	*AAW*: 4 40mm (4 × 1) AA.
	ASuW: 4 4.7in (120mm, 2 × 2) DP.
	ASW: 2 4-barrelled 375mm rocket launchers; 1 depth charge rack.
Sensors:	*Surveillance*: LW-02, DA-01, ZW-01.
	Fire control: M-45.
	Sonars: CWE-10N, PAE-1N.
Complement:	284.

These eight ships were formerly in service with the Royal Netherlands Navy. *García y García*, transferred in 1978, is the last surviving unit of the four-ship Holland class. The seven units belonging to the Friesland class were subsequently purchased as they were discarded by the Netherlands Navy, and were transferred between 1980 and 1982.

The Holland class were the first destroyers designed and built by the Royal Netherlands Navy in the immediate postwar period. Designed for air defence and anti-submarine work, they received a main armament of 120mm dual-purpose guns and 375mm rocket launchers. They differed from wartime construction in having no anti-ship torpedo tubes, and they were also fitted with indigenous air and surface surveillance radars of advanced design.

Below: A destroyer of the Friesland class training with ships of the Royal Navy off Portland, UK, before her transfer to the Peruvian Navy. The twelve ships of the Holland and Friesland classes constituted the backbone of the Dutch anti-submarine groups until the late 1970s, when they were replaced by ASW frigates of the Standaard class.

Above: The Dutch destroyers *Overijssel* (D 815) and *Rotterdam* (D 818). The photo was taken during the 1970s, following the removal of the forward pair of single 40mm guns. These two ships now serve with the Peruvian Navy as the *Coronel Bolognesi* and the *Diez Canseco*.

The Friesland class, which originally comprised eight ships, was built to a modified design. These ships have a larger hull and the same propulsion machinery as the US Gearing class (the Hollands were fitted with turbines intended for warbuilt destroyers). The major difference in equipment was the fitting of six single 40mm Bofors AA mountings; the smaller hull of the Holland class restricted them to a single 40mm gun.

Both types proved very successful in service, and the only modifications made in the ships' equipment prior to their transfer were the removal of the forward pair of 40mm mountings from the Frieslands in 1965 and the removal of the fire control systems for the remaining 40mm guns in 1977–78. The Peruvian Navy intends to modernise all eight ships and fit them out with new weapons and sensors, including Exocet anti-ship missiles.

Roger de Lauria class

Completed:	1970.
Names:	D 43 *Marqués de la Enseñada*.
Displacement:	3,012 tons standard; 3,785 tons full load.
Dimensions:	Length 391ft (119.3m) oa; beam 43ft (13m); draught 18ft 3in (5.6m).
Propulsion:	2-shaft Rateau-Bretagne geared steam turbines, 60,000shp = 28kt.
Weapons:	*ASuW*: 6 5in (127mm, 3 × 2) Mk 38 DP.
	ASW: 1 helicopter (not embarked at present); 2 triple Mk 32 tubes for Mk 44/46 torpedoes; 2 Mk 25 tubes (2 × 1) for Mk 37 torpedoes.
Sensors:	*Surveillance*: SPS-40, SPS-10B.
	Fire control: Mk 35, Mk 25.
	Sonars: SQS-32, SQA-10 VDS.
Complement:	255.

This ship was to have been one of a class of three conventional gun-armed destroyers designed in the immediate postwar period. Following problems experienced with the first ship, *Oquendo*, the still-incomplete *Marqués de la Enseñada* and her sister *Roger de Lauria* were dismantled and rebuilt to a new design. The hull was enlarged, and a new armament comprising US 5in/38 twin

Halland class

Completed:	1955–56.
Names:	J 18 *Halland*, J 19 *Småland*.
Displacement:	2,800 tons standard; 3,300 tons full load.
Dimensions:	Length 399ft (121.5m) oa; beam 41ft (12.6m); draught 18ft (5.5m) max.
Propulsion:	2-shaft geared steam turbines, 55,000shp = 35kt.
Weapons:	*AAW*: 2 57mm (1 × 2) AA, 6 40mm (6 × 1) AA.
	ASuW: 1 launcher for Saab RB-08A missiles; 4 4.7in (120mm, 2 × 2) DP; 8 21in (533mm; 1 × 5, 1 × 3) torpedo tubes.
	ASW: 2 4-barrelled 375mm rocket launchers.
Sensors:	*Surveillance*: Scanter 009, Saturn.
	Fire control: HSA M-22, PEAB 9LV 200 Mk 2.
	Sonars: 1 hull-mounted search, 1 hull-mounted attack.
Complement:	268.

Above: *Marqués de la Enseñada*, the sole survivor of three large conventionally armed destroyers built by Spain in the postwar period. The weapon/sensor outfit is entirely of US origin.

mountings and ASW torpedo tubes was fitted, but the ships were obsolescent by the time they were completed. *Marqués de la Enseñada* was badly damaged by a terrorist bomb in 1981, and although repaired by cannibalising her sister-ship (stricken January 1982) it is unlikely that she will last long, owing to persistent boiler problems.

Above: *Småland*, one of Sweden's last two destroyers. In line with Swedish neutrality policy, all the weapons are of indigenous design.

Left: *Halland* as she appeared in the late 1970s, with LW-02 radar.

Laid down in the immediate postwar period, the two destroyers of the Halland class were built to an indigenous design. Two sisters were completed for Colombia. Originally they were fitted with a Dutch LW-02 air surveillance radar and an M-45 gun fire control system, but these have now been replaced by a PEAB 9LV 200 Mk 2 FC radar atop the mainmast and an HSA M-22 FC radar atop the bridge structure. The reloadable single-ramp launcher for RB-08A anti-ship missiles was fitted in 1977–78 and is located atop the after (triple) torpedo tube mounting.

Småland was refitted in 1981–82, but was stricken in July 1984. *Halland* served as a training ship from 1980 until 1982, and was subsequently placed in reserve. The two Colombian ships were stricken in 1983–84.

Manchester class

Completed:	1982 onwards.
Names:	D 95 *Manchester*; D 96 *Gloucester*; D 97 *Edinburgh*; D 104 *York*.
Displacement:	4,100 tons standard; 5,350 tons full load.
Dimensions:	Length 463ft (141.1m) oa; beam 49ft (14.9m); draught 19ft (5.8m) max.
Propulsion:	2-shaft COGOG; 2 Olympus TM3B gas turbines, 54,400hp = 28kt; 2 Tyne RM1C gas turbines. 10,680hp = 18kt.
Weapons:	*AAW*: 1 twin launcher for Sea Dart (40 missiles); 4 30mm (2 × 2) AA, 4 20mm (4 × 1) AA. *ASuW*: 1 4.5in (114mm) Mk 8 DP. *ASW*: 1 WG.13 Lynx helicopter; 2 triple tubes for Stingray torpedoes.
Sensors:	*Surveillance*: Type 1022, Type 992Q. *Fire control*: Type 909 (2). *Sonars*: Type 2016 (Type 184M, Type 162M in D95).
Complement:	301.

Above: *Gloucester* on sea
trials in 1985. Sea Gnat
chaff dispensers have
replaced Corvus abreast the
mainmast, and there are
single 20mm guns aft.

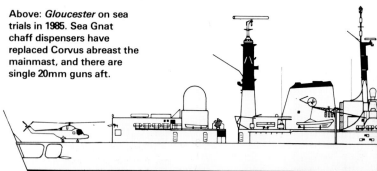

Above: The newly completed *Edinburgh* on her sea trials. The lengthened bow section has improved sea-keeping, and has created sufficient space for a much-enlarged Sea Dart magazine.

These four ships, officially designated Type 42C, are a lengthened version of the original Type 42 design. From the forward end of the bridge structure to the stern, the dimensions are identical to those of the earlier ships, but a new bow section, 53ft (16m) longer and with more sheer, has been fitted to enhance seaworthiness, to provide greater fuel capacity, and to ease the cramped accommodation spaces which had been a much-criticised feature of the Sheffield class (qv). Beam has been increased only slightly, so there has been no reduction in speed in spite of a significant increase in displacement.

The weapons systems carried are identical to those of the Sheffield class but there have been some changes in layout. The wider spacing of the 4.5in gun and the Sea Dart launcher on the lengthened forecastle has created sufficient space for a missile magazine on a par with *Bristol* (i.e. double that of the early Type 42s). *Manchester* was completed without the close-range AA weapons fitted in the wake of the Falklands conflict, and when she received this modification following trials and work-up a different arrangement was adopted from that of the earlier ships. The single BMARC 20mm mountings are fitted at bridge level on the forward superstructure, while the older-model 20mm Mk 7As are mounted in tubs abreast the after end of the hangar. *Gloucester* and the other two units have the same arrangement, and in addition their Corvus chaff launchers have been replaced by the more capable Sea Gnat system.

A variant of the Type 42 with Sea Dart launchers forward and aft was proposed in the late 1970s, but it now appears that these four ships will be the last of their type.

Below: *Manchester* as first completed, without close-range AA guns. She now has a twin 30mm BMARC mounting abaft the Searider and four single 20mm.

Sheffield class

Completed:	1975–83.
Names:	D 86 *Birmingham*; D 87 *Newcastle*; D 88 *Glasgow*; D 108 *Cardiff*; D 89 *Exeter*; D 90 *Southampton*; D 91 *Nottingham*; D 92 *Liverpool*.
Displacement:	3,150 tons standard; 4,350 tons full load.
Dimensions:	Length 410ft (125m) oa; beam 47ft (14.3m); draught 19ft (5.8m) max.
Propulsion:	2-shaft COGOG; 2 Olympus TM3B gas turbines, 54,400hp = 30kt; 2 Tyne RM1A gas turbines, 8,200hp = 18kt.
Weapons:	*AAW*: 1 twin launcher for Sea Dart (20 missiles); 4 30mm (2 × 2) AA, 4 20mm (4 × 1) AA. *ASuW*: 1 4.5in (114mm) Mk 8 DP. *ASW*: 1 WG.13 Lynx helicopter; 2 triple tubes for Stingray torpedoes.
Sensors:	*Surveillance*: Type 965M or Type 1022, Type 992Q. *Fire control*: Type 909 (2). *Sonars*: Type 184M, Type 162M.
Complement:	299.

The Type 42 design was drawn up during the late 1960s in the wake of the cancellation of the projected new generation of carriers. Staff requirements demanded a fleet escort smaller than the Type 82 capable of providing area defence for groups of ASW vessels and convoys in the North Atlantic theatre. Pressure from the Treasury to keep size down in order to minimise cost resulted in a ship which was less than ideal in a number of respects: accommodation is cramped, and endurance is lower than that of the Counties and *Bristol*.

The major innovation of the class lay in its all-gas-turbine propulsion plant, which has proved more reliable in service than the complex hybrid steam-and-gas machinery of earlier British missile destroyers. Olympus TM3B main drive turbines and Tyne RM1A cruise turbines are paired on each shaft, with all turbine uptakes being combined in a single massive funnel, and there are controllable-pitch propellers. The layout of the machinery compartments was designed to facilitate the removal of any of the four gas turbines for replacement or repair. All that is needed is a sheltered anchorage and a crane capable of lifting the turbine; the change can be carried out by the ship's own crew.

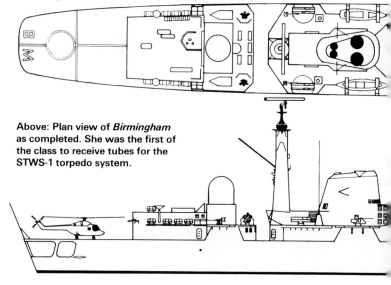

Above: Plan view of *Birmingham* as completed. She was the first of the class to receive tubes for the STWS-1 torpedo system.

Above: *Glasgow* in 1985, still with the Type 965 air search radar. Sea Dart missiles are loaded on to the launcher arms but her close-range 30mm and 20mm AA guns have been landed.

A lightweight launcher for Sea Dart was developed for these ships, which also have a less complex hand-operated magazine feed system. The installation is otherwise similar to that of *Bristol,* with Type 909 guidance radars forward and aft, but the small size of the Type 42 has restricted the number of missile reloads to half that of the Type 82. Early units of the class were fitted with the Type 965M air surveillance radar, but *Exeter* and the later vessels have the more advanced Type 1022 STIR; this has now been retrofitted to *Cardiff* and *Newcastle,* and will soon replace the Type 965M on *Glasgow* and *Birmingham.* An ADAWS-4 tactical data system is fitted.

Because the Type 42 was designed for independent operations, and not as part of a carrier task force, a manned ASW helicopter was preferred to the Ikara missile. All ships now have a circular grid fitted in the centre of the flight deck for the Harpoon securing system employed by the Lynx. The ships also have the new STWS-1 short-range ASW torpedo system, which employs triple tubes of similar design to the US Mk 32 but fires the British Stingray torpedo in place of the US Mk 46. *Birmingham* was the first to be so fitted. ▶

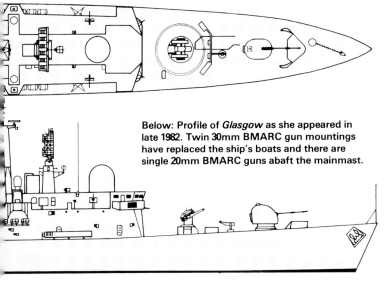

Below: Profile of *Glasgow* as she appeared in late 1982. Twin 30mm BMARC gun mountings have replaced the ship's boats and there are single 20mm BMARC guns abaft the mainmast.

A number of the Type 42s were deployed to the South Atlantic during the Falklands Conflict. Their Sea Dart missiles accounted for a number of Argentine aircraft. However, the failure of the British to provide airborne early warning aircraft for their anti-submarine carriers led to the employment of Type 42s as radar pickets with the task of intercepting aircraft attempting to attack the Task Force, and they suffered grievous losses while performing this mission. *Sheffield* was set on fire and disabled by an air-launched Exocet missile and was subsequently scuttled, and *Coventry* went down after being struck by three bombs . *Glasgow* was also hit by a bomb which entered her machinery spaces but failed to explode; she was subsequently repaired.

Experience in the South Atlantic has led to a number of modifications. The ships' boats have been removed from all units of the class and replaced by platforms carrying twin BMARC 30mm AA mountings. Further platforms have been constructed between the mainmast and the after Type 909 radar for single BMARC 20mm mountings. New electronic countermeasures equipment has been installed on platforms at the base of the mainmast, and US Mk 36 Super RBOC chaff launchers have been fitted in the bridge wings.

Below: An unidentified ship of the Sheffield class (possibly *Newcastle*) preparing to deploy to the Persian Gulf in June 1985. The block of aluminium paint on her side amidships may be an anti-missile measure. Her pennant number has been painted out.

Above: *Nottingham*, with pennant number painted out. Later ships of the class have received the Type 1022 air surveillance radar on completion, and earlier ships are now being fitted with this radar in place of the elderly Type 965. Note the close-range AA guns.

Bristol class

Completed:	1973.
Names:	D 23 *Bristol*.
Displacement:	6,100 tons standard; 7,700 tons full load.
Dimensions:	Length 507ft (154.3m) oa; beam 55ft (16.8m); draught 22ft 6in (6.8m) max.
Propulsion:	2-shaft COSAG; AEI geared steam turbines, 2 Olympus TM1A gas turbines; 30,000shp + 44,600hp = 30kt.
Weapons:	*AAW*: 1 twin launcher for Sea Dart (40 missiles); 4 30mm (2 × 2) AA, 4 20mm (4 × 1) AA.
	ASuW: 1 4.5in (114mm) Mk 8 DP.
	ASW: 1 single launcher for Ikara (32 missiles).
Sensors:	*Surveillance*: Type 965M, Type 992Q.
	Fire control: Type 909 (2), Ikara control (2).
	Sonars: Type 184M, Type 162M.
Complement:	407.

The destroyer *Bristol* was to have been the first of a class of four Type 82 carrier escorts designed to accompany a new generation of Royal Navy attack carriers projected during the early 1960s. With the cancellation of the CVA 01 in 1966 it would have been logical to scrap the entire Type 82 programme, but as the latter design was the only guided-missile destroyer on the drawing board it was decided to order a single unit of the class to serve as a trials ship for the new generation of weapons systems due to be installed in the class. An additional factor in the decision was a desire to further co-operation with the Dutch, who were due to provide an advanced radar for the Comprehensive Display System (CDS), the CF 299, to equip both the destroyers and the carriers in return for adoption of the Sea Dart surface-to-air missile by the Royal Netherlands Navy. In the event Sea Dart proved too costly and too volume-intensive for the Dutch, and the British ▶

Below: *Bristol* as she appeared in the mid-1980s, following the fitting of close-range AA guns. The guns are located on a new platform deck amidships, while a further platform has been constructed abreast the bridge structure for a pair of US Mk 36 Super RBOC chaff launchers. *Bristol* retained the Type 965 radar until mid-1985.

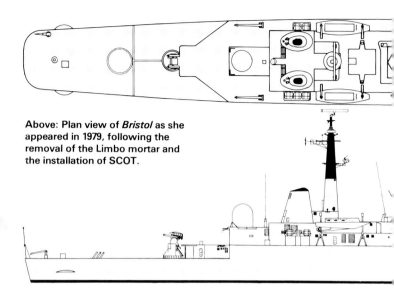

Above: Plan view of *Bristol* as she appeared in 1979, following the removal of the Limbo mortar and the installation of SCOT.

▶ decided that *Bristol* could make do with the less expensive, less capable Type 965M radar.

Sea Dart is a relatively short missile which employs a ramjet sustainer motor to give it exceptional range (50–60,000m). Unlike its predecessor, Sea Slug, it is vertically loaded from a belt-type magazine feed on to a twin-arm launcher, and semi-active guidance has replaced the beam-riding system employed with the earlier missile.

Although manned helicopters were a standard feature of British frigates by the time Bristol was designed, the Australian Ikara anti-submarine missile system was preferred, partly because of its superior all-weather availability in North Atlantic conditions, and partly because the carriers the Type 82 was designed to accompany were to have operated a squadron of large Sea King ASW helicopters.

The third new weapon system installed was the Vickers 4.5in Mk 8, which was designed as a replacement for the twin Mk 6 mounting carried by the County class.

The hybrid steam and gas turbine propulsion plant of the Counties was retained, but two Olympus TM1A gas turbines replaced the four small G6 turbines of

Right: *Bristol* as she appeared in 1984. She is considerably larger than the Type 42 air defence destroyers which succeeded her, and is therefore particularly well suited to the role of flagship, for which she has been fitted with both British and US SATCOMM systems. The Ikara launcher is located in a well abaft the 4.5in Mk 8 dual-purpose gun. Note the paired after uptakes for the Olympus gas turbines.

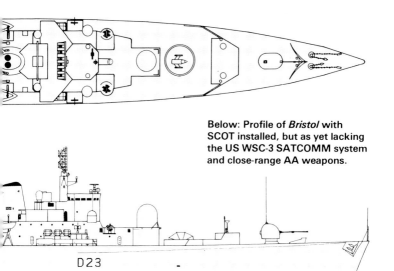

Below: Profile of *Bristol* with SCOT installed, but as yet lacking the US WSC-3 SATCOMM system and close-range AA weapons.

D23

the earlier vessels, and the after uptakes were divided into two separate funnels to facilitate removal and replacement of the gas generators.

When first completed *Bristol* conducted extensive trials of the Ikara and Sea Dart systems before entering active service. During this period she sustained serious fire damage which virtually destroyed the steam propulsion machinery, but she continued to operate on gas turbines alone and the steam plant was repaired.

During the late 1970s she was fitted out as a task force flagship, a role for which her size and ADAWS-2 tactical data system made her particularly well suited. SCOT satellite communications terminals were fitted at the after end of the bridge structure, and in 1980 the American WSC-3 SATCOMM system was added to enable her to co-operate more effectively with US naval units in the North Atlantic.

The Limbo anti-submarine mortar was removed in 1978 and the well in the quarterdeck plated over. In the wake of the Falklands conflict the ship's boats were removed and replaced by a platform deck on which twin BMARC 30mm and single BMARC 20mm AA mountings have been fitted, together with four US Mk 36 Super RBOC chaff launchers.

D23

County class

Completed:	1962–70.
Names:	D 19 *Glamorgan*; D 20 *Fife*.
Displacement:	5,440 tons standard; 6,800 tons full load.
Dimensions:	Length 521ft 6in (158.9m) oa; beam 54ft (16.4m), draught 20ft 6in (6.3m) max.
Propulsion:	2-shaft COSAG; AEI geared steam turbines, 4 G6 gas turbines; 30,000shp + 30,000hp = 30kt.
Weapons:	*AAW*: 1 twin launcher for Sea Slug Mk 2 (30 missiles); 2 quadruple launchers for Seacat in *Fife*; 2 40mm (2 × 1) AA in *Glamorgan*; 2 20mm (2 × 1) AA.
	ASuW: 4 MM38 Exocet missiles; 2 4.5in (114mm, 1 × 2) DP.
	ASW: 1 WG.13 Lynx helicopter; 2 triple tubes for Stingray torpedoes.
Sensors:	*Surveillance*: Type 965M, Type 992, Type 277.
	Fire control: Type 901, Type 903, Type 904 (2, *Fife* only).
	Sonars: Type 184M, Type 162M.
Complement:	471.

Originally a class of eight ships, the Counties were the first British guided-missile destroyers. They are large, seaworthy vessels with a useful operational radius, but are being withdrawn from service somewhat prematurely because of the obsolescence of their surface-to-air missile system. Sea Slug is a large, ungainly missile with wrap-around boosters, stowed horizontally in an inboard magazine running approximately 50 per cent of the ship's length, and is fired from a ''cage'' launcher. Its beam-riding guidance system has made it increasingly vulnerable to anti-radiation missiles, and it is now generally employed only in the anti-surface role. It has been superseded by Sea Dart.

Of the first sub-group of four ships, *Hampshire*, *Devonshire* and *Kent* were decommissioned in 1976, 1978 and 1983 respectively; only *London* survives as the Pakistani *Babur* (purchased in 1982). The four ships of the second sub-group, which were fitted with the Mk 2 model of Sea Slug and which in 1974–76 had their second 4.5in twin mounting replaced by Exocet, are still in service. *Norfolk* was sold to Chile as *Capitán Prat* in 1982, and *Antrim* (renamed *Almirante Cochrane*) followed in 1984. *Fife* and *Glamorgan* remain in service with the Royal Navy. They now operate a WG.13 Lynx helicopter.

Above: A bow view of *Glamorgan*. As completed these ships had two twin 4.5in Mk 6 mountings forward, but "B" mounting was replaced by four single launchers for MM38 Exocet anti-ship missiles in 1974–76. The Counties are large destroyers, originally designed as carrier escorts, with a full range of air defence and anti-submarine systems. However, the Sea Slug area defence missile, which employs beam riding guidance, is no longer fully operational.

Left: While operating with the South Atlantic Task Force in 1982, *Glamorgan* was struck by a shore-based Exocet coastal defence missile. She survived, but the missile destroyed the port-side Seacat launcher and its guidance radar, and this system was subsequently removed and replaced by two single 40mm guns. Both *Glamorgan* and *Fife* have been fitted with the STWS-1 anti-submarine torpedo system.

Glamorgan was struck abreast the hangar by an Argentine Exocet missile during the Falklands conflict. The fire was brought under control, but the port-side Seacat launcher and its director were destroyed, and she now has single 40mm mountings in place of the Seacat system. Triple torpedo tubes for the STWS-1 system are now fitted in both ships, and both now operate the WG.13 Lynx in place of the Wessex HAS.3 helicopters formerly carried. Platforms for US Mk 36 chaff launchers have been constructed abreast the forward superstructure.

Udaloy class

Completed: 1981 onwards.
Names: *Udaloy; Vitse Admiral Kulakov; Marshal Vasil'yevsky; Marshal Zhakarov; Admiral Spiridonov.*
Displacement: 6,200–6,700 tons standard; 8,200 tons full load.
Dimensions: Length 531ft (162m); beam 63ft (19.3m); draught 20ft (6.2m).
Propulsion: 2-shaft COGAG; 4 gas turbines each of 25,000hp; 100,000hp = 32kt.
Weapons: *AAW:* 8 vertical SA-N-8 launchers (64 missiles); 2 3.9in (100mm, 2 × 1) DP; 4 30mm Gatlings.
ASW: 2 Ka-27 Helix-A helicopters; 2 quadruple launchers for SS-N-14 missiles; 2 12-barrelled RBU 6000 rocket launchers; 8 21in (533mm, 2 × 4) torpedo tubes.
Sensors: *Surveillance:* Strut Pair (2) in first two units; Top Plate/Top Mesh, Strut Pair in others; Palm Frond (3).
Fire control: Eye Bowl (2), ?? (2 for SA-N-8), Kite Screech, Bass Tilt (2).
Sonars: 1 hull-mounted LF, 1 LF VDS.
Complement: 300.

The destroyers of the Udaloy class are the latest in a succession of Soviet "large anti-submarine ships" (BPKs). Unlike their immediate predecessors of the Kresta-II class, which although designated "cruisers" in the West are of similar size, they have no area air defence system, but are dedicated exclusively to anti-submarine warfare. In terms of their overall capabilities they closely resemble the US Navy's Spruance class (qv), and the latter type, which entered service some six years before *Udaloy*, appears to have exerted considerable influence on the Soviet design. ▶

Above: A destroyer of the *Udaloy* class at speed. The large hull gives these ships superior sea-keeping performance and greater endurance than earlier Soviet ASW destroyers. In size they compare with the US Navy's Spruance class, and the similarities extend to the primary anti-submarine mission and the propulsion machinery.

Below: *Udaloy* photographed on exercise in the North Atlantic in 1984. Unlike their predecessors of the Kresta II and Kara classes, these BPKs have no area defence system, but they carry two anti-submarine helicopters and are fitted with more capable sonars. They have a similar hull-form to the patrol ships of the Krivak class, of which they are in effect a much-enlarged version. The paired funnels house the uptakes for four large gas turbines, capable of driving the ships at speeds in excess of 30kt. Construction of these formidable ships continues.

Above: *Udaloy* on sea trials in 1981. The main armament is aboard but there are empty platforms atop the bridge and hangars for the SA-N-8 missile guidance radars. There are also empty platforms on either side of the mainmast for electronic countermeasures antennas.

▶ Propulsion is by four large gas turbines, each of 25–30,000hp, disposed in a COGAG unit arrangement with distinctive paired funnels. The turbine machinery, together with its uptakes and air intakes, occupies the entire centre part of the ship. In consequence, all the major weapons systems are disposed fore and aft.

Udaloy is the first Soviet BPK to operate two helicopters for anti-submarine work. These are housed and maintained in twin hangars which exit on to a flight deck above the stern. The Ka-25 Hormone-A which operated from earlier BPKs has been superseded by the Ka-27 Helix-A, an improved model with more internal volume and more advanced avionics. Like its predecessor, the Helix is a twin-rotor helicopter, and its exceptional height as compared with equivalent Western types means that it can be accommodated in its hangar only by combining a retractable hangar roof and a hangar floor which acts as a lift to lower the helicopter to main deck level.

The remaining anti-submarine systems installed in *Udaloy* are common to other major Soviet ASW vessels: the SS-N-14 missile system, for which there are fixed quadruple launchers beneath the bridge wings, quadruple torpedo tubes, and RBU 6000 rocket launchers. The bow-mounted and variable-depth sonars are powerful low-frequency models, and are probably the same as those installed in the "battlecruiser" *Kirov*.

For air defence a new Soviet SAM system will be installed. The SA-N-8 system employs a vertically launched missile which is housed in a cylindrical magazine some 2m (6ft) in diameter holding six missile rounds. Four of these VL tubes are countersunk into the forecastle, and four further installations are mounted between the after funnels and the helicopter hangar. The SA-N-8

Below: Profile of *Udaloy* as completed. The vertical launch canisters are located on the forecastle and abaft the second pair of funnels.

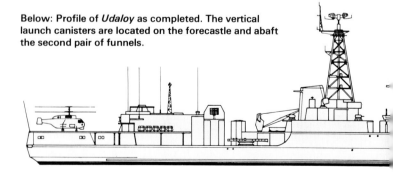

system is not yet fully operational, and all ships of the class have so far been completed without the missile fire control radars, which will be mounted on circular platforms above the bridge and the hangar. Two single 100mm guns are mounted forward of the bridge, and there are the standard Soviet anti-missile systems, comprising four 30mm Gatlings (abreast the second pair of funnels) and twin-barrelled chaff launchers (close to the bow).

The Udaloys have no anti-ship weapons, although the single 100mm guns have a limited anti-surface capability. They would probably be integrated with other destroyers armed with SSMs when engaging in ASW operations in areas where they might encounter hostile surface units.

The first two ships, *Udaloy* and *Kulakov*, were fitted only with a medium-range 2-D back-to-back air surveillance radar (Strut Pair), but the third and fourth ships, which were completed in late 1983, have a new 3-D antenna, designated Top Plate/Top Mesh, to provide target data to the SA-N-8 missile system.

Above: *Udaloy* in company with an anti-submarine destroyer of the Kanin class during an exercise in the North Atlantic.

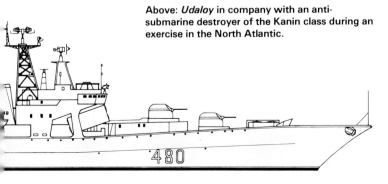

Kashin class

Completed:	1963–72.
Names:	*Obraztsovy*; *Odarenny*; *Steregushchy*; *Komsomolets Ukrainy*; *Krasny Kavkaz*; *Krasny Krym*; *Provorny*; *Reshitelny*; *Skory*; *Smetlivy*; *Soobrazitelny*; *Sposobny*; *Strogy*.
Displacement:	3,750 tons standard; 4,750 tons full load.
Dimensions:	Length 472ft (144m); beam 52ft (15.8m); draught 16ft (4.8m).
Propulsion:	2-shaft COGAG; 4 gas turbines each of 24,000hp; 96,000hp = 35kt.
Weapons:	*AAW*: 2 twin SA-N-1 launchers (44 Goa missiles); 4 3in (76mm, 2 × 2) DP.
	ASW: 2 12-barrelled RBU 6000 rocket launchers; 2 6-barrelled RBU 1000 rocket launchers; 5 21in (533mm, 1 × 5) torpedo tubes.
Sensors:	*Surveillance*: Head Net-A (2) or Big Net, Head Net-C; Don-2 (2) or Don Kay (2).
	Fire control: Peel Group (2), Owl Screech (2).
	Sonars: 1 hull-mounted MF.
Complement:	280.

Above: One of the earlier units of the Kashin
class, seen here at anchor in the
Mediterranean. She has twin Head Net-A air
search radars. These ships are notable for the
symmetrical layout of their weapons
systems. Note the distinctive paired uptakes
for the four gas turbines.

Above: This unit of the Kashin class has the standard
combination of Big Net and Head Net-C air surveillance radars.

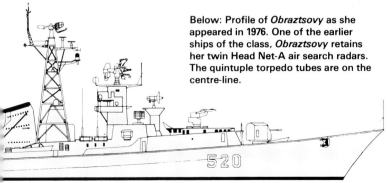

Below: Profile of *Obraztsovy* as she
appeared in 1976. One of the earlier
ships of the class, *Obraztsovy* retains
her twin Head Net-A air search radars.
The quintuple torpedo tubes are on the
centre-line.

▶ The Kashin class were built as large multi-purpose destroyers with good AAW and ASW capabilities. Their primary mission as originally conceived may have been to provide additional protection to Kynda class cruisers in their anti-carrier role. The Kashins, however, proved more successful in service than the Kyndas, and continued in series production in both the Baltic and the Black Sea throughout the 1960s.

The most remarkable technological achievement of the design lay in its all-gas-turbine propulsion plant. Although a number of NATO navies were already experimenting with gas turbines in hybrid combinations, the installed horsepower of the Kashin remained unmatched in the West until the completion of the light aircraft carrier HMS *Invicible* in 1980. Four large industrial gas-turbines, each of about 24,000hp, were installed, the uptakes being led up into distinctive paired funnels angled outboard to keep the hot gases clear of the radars. Following sea trials, the forward pair of funnels had to be heightened.

The Kashins were the first Soviet ships with a "double-ended" SAM system. An unusual feature of the launchers is that they reload while trained to port and starboard respectively, suggesting a modular launcher/magazine installation. Early ships carried two single Head Net-A air search radars atop the two lattice masts, but ships completed in the mid/late 1960s had the second antenna

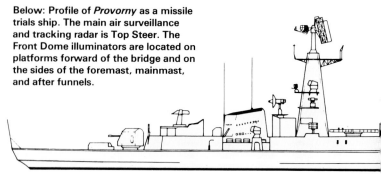

Below: Profile of *Provorny* as a missile trials ship. The main air surveillance and tracking radar is Top Steer. The Front Dome illuminators are located on platforms forward of the bridge and on the sides of the foremast, mainmast, and after funnels.

replaced by the longer-range Big Net aerial, and the first by a back-to-back Head Net-C; some of the older units have recently been fitted with two Head Net-C antennae in place of Head Net-A.

The ASW armament comprises anti-submarine rocket launchers and torpedo tubes amidships. Some Kashins have a helicopter landing pad marked out on the stern, but in others of the class this has been painted over. Although Ka-25 Hormone-A helicopters can be operated, there is no hangar, nor even any maintenance facilities.

From 1971 onwards some ships of the Kashin class were converted as "rocket ships" (see Kashin-Mod class), and in the mid-1970s *Provorny* was fitted out as a trials ship for the new SA-N-7 medium-range surface-to-air missile. Both SA-N-1 launchers have been removed in the latter vessel, together with their Peel Group guidance radars. There is now a single-arm launcher for SA-N-7 missiles aft, with two further positions (as yet unoccupied) forward of the bridge. Guidance for the missiles is provided by the large Top Steer 3-D tracking radar, located atop a new plated mast forward of the second funnel, and by eight small Front Dome illuminators distributed evenly forward and aft. The original lattice mainmast has been removed and the bridge tower rebuilt to accommodate a Head Net-C air search radar.

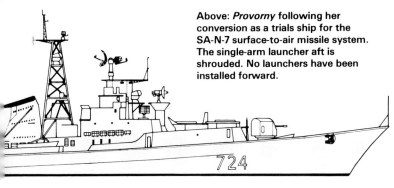

Above: *Provorny* following her conversion as a trials ship for the SA-N-7 surface-to-air missile system. The single-arm launcher aft is shrouded. No launchers have been installed forward.

724

Kanin class

Completed: 1961–62 (converted 1968–77).
Names: *Boiky, Derzky, Gnevny, Gordy, Gremyashchy, Uporny, Zhguchy, Zorky.*
Displacement: 3,700 tons standard; 4,750 tons full load.
Dimensions: Length 456ft (139m) oa; beam 48ft (15m); draught 16ft (5m).
Propulsion: 2-shaft geared steam turbines 84,000shp = 34kt.
Weapons: *AAW*: 1 twin SA-N-1 launcher (22 Goa missiles); 8 57mm (2 × 4) AA; 8 30mm (4 × 2) AA.
ASW: 3 12-barrelled RBU 6000 rocket launchers; 10 21in (533mm, 2 × 5) torpedo tubes.
Sensors: *Surveillance*: Head Net-C, Don Kay (2).
Fire control: Peel Group, Hawk Screech, Drum Tilt (2).
Sonars: 1 hull-mounted MF.
Complement: 300.

These eight ships were originally "rocket ships" of the Krupny class, armed with SS-N-1 launchers for Scrubber anti-ship missiles forward and aft and four

quadruple 57mm AA mountings. When the SS-N-1 became obsolescent in the mid-1960s, it was decided to convert the vessels as ASW ships on a similar pattern to the Kotlin SAM. The conversions were undertaken at the Zhdanov Yard, Leningrad, and later at Komsomolsk in the Pacific, from 1968 to 1977.

An SA-N-1 launcher was installed aft atop its own magazine and a tower for the Peel Group guidance radar was constructed forward of the second funnel. Only two quadruple 57mm mountings were retained forward. Whereas little modification had been made to ASW capabilities in the Kotlin conversion (see Kotlin SAM class), the Kanin had a new medium-frequency bow sonar installed and three RBU 6000 rocket launchers fitted, two of them abreast the tower mast and the third on the forecastle. The twin banks of torpedo tubes were expanded from triple to quintuple mountings. The bridge was enlarged and the electronics updated. A helicopter platform was fitted aft, but no maintenance facilities were provided. All the Kanins now have four twin 30mm mountings abreast the second funnel and Drum Tilt FC radars installed on platforms projecting from the radar tower.

The Kanin class appear to be much more successful conversions than the smaller Kotlin SAMs, and have far superior ASW qualities, although the weapons themselves are somewhat dated. Most ships of the class serve either with the Northern or the Pacific Fleets.

Left: The most prominent feature of the Kanin class destroyers as converted are the twin-arm launcher for SA-N-1 Goa missiles and the distinctive Peel Group guidance radar atop its squat tower mast. The air surveillance radar is a Head Net-C "back-to-back" system.

Below: A destroyer of the Kanin class on exercise in the North Atlantic. In spite of the predominance of air defence weapons these ships are designated "large anti-submarine ships" (BPKs) by the Soviet Navy.

Kotlin SAM class

Completed:	1954–58 (converted 1962–72).
Names:	*Bravy; Nakhodchivy; Nastoychivy; Nesokrushimy; Skromny; Skrytny; Soznatel'ny; Vozbuzhdenny.*
Displacement:	2,700 tons standard; 3,600 tons full load.
Dimensions:	Length 415ft (126.5m) oa; beam 42ft (13m); draught 15ft (4.6m).
Propulsion:	2-shaft geared steam turbines; 72,000shp = 36kt.
Weapons:	*AAW*: 1 twin SA-N-1 launcher (22 Goa missiles); 4 45mm (1 × 4) AA; 8 30mm (4 × 2) AA in some ships (see below). *ASuW*: 2 5.1in (130mm, 1 × 2) DP. *ASW*: 2 12-barrelled RBU 6000 rocket launchers; 5 21in (533mm, 1 × 5) torpedo tubes.
Sensors:	*Surveillance*: Head Net-C (Head Net-A in *Bravy*); Don-2 (1/2). *Fire control*: Peel Group, Sun Visor, Hawk Screech, Drum Tilt (2). *Sonars*: 1 hull-mounted MF.
Complement:	300.

In 1962 the first missile conversion of a Kotlin class destroyer was completed. The ship chosen, *Bravy,* served as an experimental prototype for two years before further ships were taken in hand for conversion. The principal modifica-

tion was the installation of a twin SA-N-1 launcher atop its own magazine in place of the after 130mm and 45mm mountings. A prominent pyramid-shaped tower mast carrying the Peel Group missile guidance radar replaced the former small lattice mast. A new after funnel was designed to double as a blast deflector for the missiles. Initially, the midships 45mm mountings and the torpedo tubes were removed, but they were restored in 1964.

Eight further units were converted between 1966 and 1972, of which *Spravedlivy* was transferred to Poland as the *Warszawa* in 1970. The original Kotlin funnel was retained in these ships and the radar tower differed in shape from that of *Bravy*. The midships 45mm were again discarded, although four ships — *Nesokrushimy, Skrytny, Soznatel'ny* and *Vozbuzhdenny* — were fitted with four twin 30mm mountings in their place, together with Drum Tilt FC radars. The original 16-barrelled, hand-loaded anti-submarine rocket launchers were replaced by automatic RBU 6000s (except in *Skromny*) and the air surveillance radar was updated.

Topweight problems may have been a factor in the decision to convert only nine units of the Kotlin class. Although deployed to all four Soviet Fleets, the majority of the Kotlin SAMs serve in the Black Sea and the Pacific.

Below: The Kotlin SAM was the first Soviet missile ship conversion. The after twin 130mm and quadruple 45mm gun mountings were removed and replaced by a magazine deckhouse and launcher for SA-N-1 Goa missiles. The bulky tower mast and Peel Group guidance radar may have caused topweight problems. This particular unit is one of the second series of conversions, with the original Kotlin funnel.

Sovremenny class

Completed:	1981 onwards.
Names:	*Sovremenny*; *Otchayanny*; *Otlichny*; *Osmotritelny*.
Displacement:	6,300 tons standard; 7,900 tons full load.
Dimensions:	Length 522ft (159m) oa; beam 56ft (17m); draught 20ft (6.1m) max.
Propulsion:	2-shaft geared steam turbines; 100,000shp = 34kt.
Weapons:	*AAW*: 2 single SA-N-7 launchers (48? missiles); 4 30mm Gatlings.
	ASuW: 2 quadruple launchers for SS-N-22 missiles; 1 Ka-25 Hormone-B missile-targeting helicopter; 4 5.1in (130mm, 2 × 2) DP.
	ASW: 2 6-barrelled RBU 1000 rocket launchers; 4 21in (533mm, 2 × 2) torpedo tubes.
Sensors:	*Surveillance*: Top Steer, Palm Frond (3).
	Fire control: Band Stand, Kite Screech, Front Dome (6), Bass Tilt (2).
	Sonars: 1 hull-mounted MF.
Complement:	380.

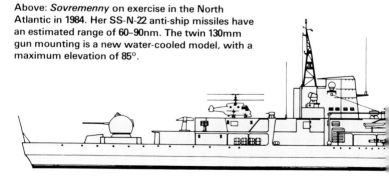

Above: *Sovremenny* on exercise in the North
Atlantic in 1984. Her SS-N-22 anti-ship missiles have
an estimated range of 60–90nm. The twin 130mm
gun mounting is a new water-cooled model, with a
maximum elevation of 85°.

Above: The Sovremenny class are the first Soviet destroyers to be built for a primary anti-surface mission since the early 1960s. They are apparently designated *eskadrenny minonosets* — the traditional Soviet "destroyer" classification.

The destroyers of the Sovremenny class are the surface warfare counterparts of the Udaloy class anti-submarine vessels (qv). However, although they are contemporaries of the latter — the lead ships of both types were completed in the same year — no attempt has been made to standardise the hull-form, the propulsion machinery, or the weapons systems carried. While the *Udaloy* is a completely new design, the hull and the machinery of the *Sovremenny* is essentially that of the ASW cruisers of the Kresta-II class, the principal differences being the raised forecastle and the broader stern section. A single central funnel permits a larger number of weapons systems to be carried on the centre-line — a feature which favours the ship's secondary mission of air defence.

The anti-ship missile, housed in quadruple launchers beneath the bridge wings, is the SS-N-22. It is thought to be an updated sea-skimming variant of the SS-N-9, with which it shares the distinctive Band Stand guidance radar, housed within a GRP radome atop the bridge. Maximum ranges of 55–90nm (100–170km) are generally quoted by reference sources. Over-the-horizon targeting data is provided by a Ka-25 Hormone-B helicopter, for which a telescopic hangar is provided immediately abaft the funnel.

The other major anti-surface system is the 130mm gun, a new fully-automatic water-cooled model in a twin high-angle mounting; *Sovremenny* has one mounting on the forecastle and a second on the quarterdeck. Fire control in both the anti-surface and anti-aircraft modes is provided by a single Kite Screech radar located atop the bridge. The mounting has been designed as a successor to the twin 130mm mounting of the Kotlin class, and provides the Soviet Navy with a powerful fire support weapon at a time when the older gun-armed surface units are being steadily decommissioned due to their advanced age.

Inboard of the twin 130mm mountings are launchers for the SA-N-7 area defence missile. This is believed to be similar in performance to the US Navy's ▶

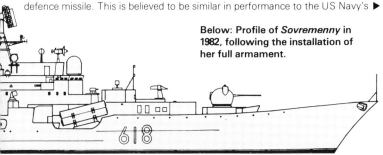

Below: Profile of *Sovremenny* in 1982, following the installation of her full armament.

▶ Standard SM-1 MR missile, with a maximum effective range of about 25,000m. The single launcher is similar in configuration to the US Navy's Mk 13, and the SA-N-7 is the first Soviet shipborne SAM to employ semi-active guidance on the Western pattern. Target data is provided by the large Top Steer 3-D antenna (superseded in the fourth unit of the class by a new combination designated Top Plate/Top Steer), and there are six small illuminators (Front Dome) disposed to port and to starboard. For close-in defence against anti-ship missiles there are the standard 30mm Gatlings, and twin-barrelled chaff launchers on the stern.

Right: *Sovremenny* running sea trials in the Baltic in 1980. She was completed without any of her major weapons systems but with most of her electronics outfit in place. The large radome atop the bridge structure houses the Band Stand guidance radar for the SS-N-22 anti-ship missiles. The air search/tracking radar is Top Steer.

Below: Another view of *Sovremenny* in 1984. In addition to her powerful battery of anti-surface weapons she is fitted with the SA-N-7 medium-range air defence system. There are single-arm launchers forward and aft, and six small Front Dome tracker radars disposed around the superstructure. Anti-submarine capabilities are relatively limited for a ship of this size.

Anti-submarine capability is minimal, being sufficient only for the ship's own immediate defence purposes. The only ASW weapons are torpedoes (amidships) and two RBU 1000 rocket launchers (abreast the after end of the helicopter deck). A medium-frequency sonar of moderate performance is fitted, but there is no variable-depth sonar.

Sovremenny is essentially a general-purpose destroyer which will be employed in conjunction with other vessels for a variety of tasks, including the engagement of hostile surface units and the support of amphibious landings.

Kashin-Mod class

Completed: 1964–71 (converted 1973–80).
Names: *Ognevoy*; *Slavny*; *Sderzhanny*; *Smel'ny*; *Smyshlenny*; *Stroyny*.
Displacement: 3,950 tons standard; 4,950 tons full load.
Dimensions: Length 480ft (146m) oa; beam 52ft (15.8m); draught 16ft (4.8m).
Propulsion: 2-shaft COGAG; 4 gas turbines each of 24,000hp; 96,000hp = 35kt.
Weapons: *AAW*: 2 twin SA-N-1 launchers (44 Goa missiles); 4 3in (76mm, 2 × 2) DP; 4 30mm Gatlings.
ASuW: 4 single launchers for SS-N-2C missiles.
ASW: 2 12-barrelled RBU 6000 rocket launchers; 5 21in (533mm, 1 × 5) torpedo tubes.
Sensors: *Surveillance*: Big Net, Head Net-C, Don Kay (2).
Fire control: Peel Group (2), Owl Screech (2), Bass Tilt (2).
Sonars: 1 hull-mounted MF, 1 MF VDS.
Complement: 320.

Beginning in 1971, six ships of the Kashin class, including one unit then still under construction, were taken in hand for conversion as "rocket ships". Four SS-N-2C horizon-range anti-ship missiles were fitted abreast the after superstructure; variable-depth sonar was installed on a remodelled stern, increasing length overall by some two metres (6ft), and a helicopter platform was built above it; and the after pair of RBU 1000 rocket launchers was removed and

Above: The aft-firing SS-N-2C anti-ship missile launchers are particularly prominent in this stern view. The flight deck and variable-depth sonar were also fitted during conversion.

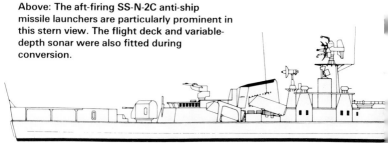

Above: The Kashin-Mod class is designed for a close shadowing role. One or other of these ships or a vessel of the Kildin class is frequently to be seen in company with a US Navy carrier, especially in the Mediterranean, where the US Sixth Fleet provides vital support to NATO's southern flank. A close watch is also kept on NATO amphibious exercises on the northern flank, enabling a valuable "information" bank fo be built up.

replaced by a new deckhouse on which were mounted four anti-missile 30mm Gatlings together with their Bass Tilt FC radars. The major air defence systems were retained. *Ognevoy*, the first unit converted, initially retained the Head Net-A radars with which she was initially completed, but now has the standard combination of Head Net-C and Big Net.

Four of the six ships serve with the Black Sea Fleet, and when operating in the Eastern Mediterranean have frequently been employed as "shadows" for the carriers of the US Sixth Fleet. It is thought that if an outbreak of hostilities were imminent they would attempt a pre-emptive strike, using their aft-firing S S-N-2C missiles, and extricate themselves as quickly as possible using the rapid response of their gas turbine propulsion.

It was at first thought that the entire Kashin class would be similarly modified, but the programme now appears to have been terminated. Excessive topweight may have been a problem with the converted units, as a considerable amount of new equipment has been installed for the loss of only two small ASW rocket launchers. Alternatively, the expansion of new surface ship construction during the 1970s may have precluded the extension of the programme beyond six units, either because of cost factors or as a result of labour shortages.

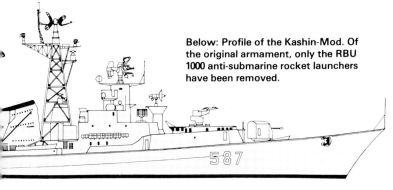

Below: Profile of the Kashin-Mod. Of the original armament, only the RBU 1000 anti-submarine rocket launchers have been removed.

Kildin class

Completed: 1958 (converted 1973–75).
Names: *Bedovy*; *Neulovimy*; *Prozorlivy*.
Displacement: 2,800 tons standard; 3,700 tons full load.
Dimensions: Length 415ft (126.5m) oa; beam 42ft (13m); draught 18ft 9in (5.7m) max.
Propulsion: 2-shaft geared steam turbines 72,000shp = 35kt.
Weapons: *AAW*: 4 3in (76mm, 2 × 2) DP; 16 57/45mm (4 × 4) AA.
ASuW: 4 single launchers for SS-N-2C missiles.
ASW: 2 12-barrelled RBU 6000 rocket launchers; 4 21in (533mm, 2 × 2) torpedo tubes.
Sensors: *Surveillance*: Head Net-C (Strut Pair in *Bedovy*); Don-2 (2).
Fire control: Owl Screech, Hawk Screech (2).
Sonars: 1 hull-mounted HF.
Complement: 300.

As originally completed, the four Kildin class ships were missile conversions of the conventional Kotlin class destroyer. A single bulky launcher for the SS-N-1 Scrubber anti-ship missile was fitted aft, together with a large magazine. The remaining armament comprised two quadruple 57mm mountings (45mm in *Bedovy*) forward of the bridge, a further two 57mm mountings abreast the mainmast, twin torpedo tubes amidships, and anti-submarine rocket launchers close to the bow.

By the late 1960s the SS-N-1 missile was obsolescent and was already being removed from the later Krupny class, which underwent an ASW conversion. It

Below: A destroyer of the Kildin class following conversion. The SS-N-1 launcher and magazine originally fitted aft has been replaced by a new deckhouse and two twin 76.2mm dual-purpose gun mountings. On either side of the deckhouse there are two fixed launchers for SS-N-2C anti-ship missiles. The original four quadruple 57mm AA mountings (two forward, two amidships) have been retained. The original radar outfit has been considerably modified. The Flat Spin and Slim Net search and targeting radars have been replaced by a Head Net-C V-beam antenna atop the foremast, and the original Hawk Screech fire control radars for the 57mm guns have been supplemented by an Owl Screech GFCS for the 76.2mm guns. *Bedovy* has broader funnels than her sister-ships.

Above: *Prozorlivy* approaches the US Navy command ship *Mount Whitney* during the NATO exercise "Northern Wedding" in 1982. Ships of this class and the Modified Kashin class are frequently employed as "shadows" for major NATO surface units, especially aircraft carriers. Both types have been fitted with aft-firing launchers for the horizon-range SS-N-2C missile.

was then decided to take in hand three of the Kildin class ships in order to update them, and the conversions were duly completed at Nikolayev between 1973 and 1975. The SS-N-1 launcher was removed and replaced by two twin 76mm mountings, and an Owl Screech FC radar was installed atop the short lattice mainmast. Anti-ship capability was restored, however, by fitting four cylindrical launchers for the SS-N-2C horizon-range missile abreast the after structure. *Neulovimy* and *Prozorlivy* received a Head Net-C air surveillance radar, but *Bedovy* was fitted with the prototype Strut Pair radar, which was later to be installed in the Udaloy class. She can also be distinguished from her two modernised sisters by her broader funnels.

The modified ships are frequently deployed as "shadows" for the big US Navy carriers, in similar fashion to the modified Kashins (qv). The fourth unit of the class, *Neuderzhimy*, which serves with the Pacific Fleet, remains unconverted and is probably in reserve.

Kotlin class

Completed:	1954–58.
Names:	*Bessledny; Blagorodny*; Blestyashchy*; Burlivy*; Byvaly*; Dal'nevostochny Komsomolets; Moskovsky Komsomolets*; Naporisty*; Plamenny*; Speshny; Spokoyny; Svedushchy*; Svetly; Vesky; Vdokhnovenny*; Vliyatel'ny; Vozmushchenny; Vyderzhanny*; Vyzyvayushchy*.*
Displacement:	2,600 tons standard; 3,500 tons full load.
Dimensions:	Length 415ft (126.5m) oa; beam 42ft (13m); draught 15ft (4.6m).
Propulsion:	2-shaft geared steam turbines 72,000shp = 36kt.
Weapons:	*AAW*: 16 45mm (4×4) AA; 4/8 25mm (2/4×2) AA. *ASuW*: 4 5.1in (130mm) DP; 5/10 21in (533mm, 1/2×5). *ASW*: 2 16-barrelled RBU 2500, 2 6-barrelled RBU 600 rocket launchers in Modified *Kotlin* only; 6 BMB-2 D/C projectors in unmodified ships.
Sensors:	*Surveillance*: Slim Net, Neptune or Don-2 (1/2). *Fire control*: Sun Visor, Hawk Screech (2). *Sonars*: 1 hull-mounted HF.
Complement:	336.
	*Modified units

The Kotlin class were the last conventional destroyers built for the Soviet Navy. Similar in layout to their predecessors of the Skory class, the Kotlins incorporated a number of new technical developments, including stabilised turrets for the dual-purpose 130mm guns and a new quadruple 45mm mounting. The result was a powerful, seaworthy design, but one which was already outdated by the time the first unit was completed. The construction programme was therefore terminated in favour of new designs armed with anti-ship missiles.

From 1962 onwards, nine units of the class was converted to carry surface-to-

Below: An unmodified destroyer of the Kotlin class, with the two quintuple banks of torpedo tubes originally fitted. An outstanding design in its day, the Kotlin is now obsolescent, and is used primarily for training and fire support.

Above: A number of units of the Kotlin class have had the second bank of torpedo tubes removed, and have received four twin 25mm AA mountings. RBU 2500 rocket launchers have also been fitted in order to improve anti-submarine capabilities.

air missiles (see Kotlin SAM class). Eleven more units underwent a modification programme aimed at updating their ASW capability. RBU 2500 rocket launchers were installed on either side of the forward 45mm mounting and the after bank of torpedo tubes was landed to compensate. Later conversions also had a pair of six-barrelled RBU 600 rocket launchers on the stern, while some ships had the automatic RBU 6000 in place of the hand-loaded RBU 2500. During the 1970s the modified ships received four twin 25mm mountings, while unmodified units received two twin mountings. Three vessels were also fitted with helicopter platforms, but these were removed from all except *Svetly*. *Moskovsky Komsomolets* had a variable-depth sonar installed on her stern in 1978.

The Kotlins are now being steadily decommissioned, and those that remain are employed largely for training. Their only military value lies in their heavy gun armament, which would still be of use in fire-support operations.

Arleigh Burke class

Completed: 1989 onwards.
Names: DDG 51 *Arleigh Burke*.
Displacement: 6,500 tons light; 8,400 tons full load.
Dimensions: Length 504ft (153.5m); beam 67ft (20.4m); draught 20ft (6.1m).
Propulsion: 2-shaft COGAG; 4 General Electric LM 2500 gas turbines; 100,000hp = 30kt.
Weapons: *AAW*: Standard SM-2 MR missiles from 2 Mk 41 vertical launch modules (29 + 61 max.); 2 20mm Phalanx CIWS.
ASuW: Tomahawk missiles from Mk 41 VL modules; 2 quadruple launchers for Harpoon missiles; 1 5in (127mm) Mk 45 DP.
ASW: 2 triple Mk 32 tubes for Mk 46/50 torpedoes; VL ASROC missiles from Mk 41 modules.
Sensors: *Surveillance*: SPY-1D (4), SPS-67.
Fire control: SPG-62 (3), Seafire GFCS.
Sonars: SQS-53C, SQR-19 TACTAS.
Complement: 339.

The origins of the Arleigh Burke design lie in the requirement to replace the numerous air defence escorts which were built for the US Navy in the early 1960s to protect the carrier task forces and which now pose the problem of "block obsolescence". Current plans envisage the construction of 29 units by 1994–95 to replace the DDGs of the Charles F. Adams and Coontz classes, with the possibility that further ships will be ordered when the Leahy and Belknap classes become due for replacement. The destroyers of the Arleigh Burke class will supplement the Aegis cruisers in support of the 15 carrier battle groups (CVBG) and the four surface action groups (SAG), and will also be employed to protect replenishment and amphibious groups.

The weapons systems technology is essentially similar to that of the Ticonderoga class cruisers. The Aegis air defence system, which is based on four fixed SPY-1D arrays, the Standard SM-2 MR missile, two Phalanx 20mm CIWS, and active and passive countermeasures, can handle saturation attacks by aircraft or missiles, including sea-skimmers. There is also a formidable anti-surface capablity in the form of medium-range Harpoon and long-range ▶

Below: An artist's impression of the *Arleigh Burke*. The Mk 41 vertical launch modules for Standard and Tomahawk missiles can be seen forward of the bridge structure and abaft the second funnel. The forward magazine accommodates 29 missiles, the after one 61.

Above: Artist's impression of *Arleigh Burke* launching a Tomahawk missile. There are facilities for landing and refuelling a helicopter, but no hangar is provided.

Above right: An eight-cell vertical launch module being lowered into place aboard a cruiser of the Ticonderoga class. The latter vessels have a number of systems in common with the new destroyers.

▶ Tomahawk anti-ship missiles, plus a single 5in/54cal. Mk 45 gun, mounted on the forecastle. Tomahawk and Standard will be fired from the Martin-Marietta Mk 41 vertical launch system, but Harpoon will be fired from the standard canisters. The Seafire gun fire control system, if developed and funded, will enable the 5in gun to fire laser-guided projectiles against subsonic aircraft, small surface targets and shore positions.

In order to make the new design less costly than the Ticonderoga class some reduction in capabilities was necessary. Only three SPG-62 tracker/illuminators are provided, resulting in a reduction of 25 per cent in the number of air targets that can be engaged simultaneously. However, the principal difference between the two classes lies in the area of anti-submarine warfare: there is no helicopter hangar (although a helicopter can be landed on the stern and refuelled), and ASW missiles will not be carried until vertical-launch ASROC (currently under development) becomes available for firing from the Mk 41 VL system. Nevertheless, to enable the ships to participate fully in battle group operations, the latest hull-mounted and towed sonars will be fitted, and an advanced tactical data system based on the new UYK-43 computer will enable target data to be

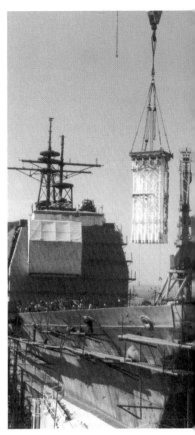

transmitted in real time to similarly equipped units, giving effective capabilities beyond the year 2000.

Unlike the cruisers of the Ticonderoga class, which were based on the Spruance design dating from the late 1960s, the Arleigh Burke is a completely new type incorporating a number of features novel to US Navy construction. Great attention has been paid to the ship's ability to resist action damage. Whereas earlier US cruiser and destroyer designs made extensive use of aluminium in order to maximise superstructure volume without exceeding topweight limits, the Arleigh Burke class will be constructed entirely of steel, and will therefore be more resistant to blast and fire damage. A single superstructure block accommodates all four of the SPY-1 radar arrays, and the combat information centre is located within the hull at main deck level, as is the communications office. The sonar room is not adjacent to the CIC, but is located well forward, and the distributed data processing system is designed to prevent the ship from being disabled by a single lucky hit. Sloping superstructure sides reduce the radar cross-section of the ship by avoiding corner reflectors, and all vital spaces, including the vertical launch modules, are to be protected by Kevlar armour.

The adoption of all-steel construction has inevitably made hull volume a more critical factor in the ship's design. The unusually broad waterplane selected brings with it improved sea-keeping qualities, but at the expense of reduced endurance, as more power (and consequently fuel) is required to drive the ship through the water. The four LM 2500 gas turbines have been uprated to 25,000hp, giving a 25 per cent increase in power over the Spruance derivatives. Congress is pressing for a RACER waste-heat recovery system, but the US Navy is not entirely happy with the resultant additional maintenance load.

USA
Kidd class

Completed:	1981–82.
Names:	DDG 993 *Kidd*; DDG 994 *Callaghan*; DDG 995 *Scott*; DDG 996 *Chandler*.
Displacement:	6,210 tons light; 9,300 tons full load.
Dimensions:	Length 563ft (171.7m) oa; beam 55ft (16.8m); draught 31ft 6in (9.6m) max.
Propulsion:	2-shaft COGAG; 4 General Electric LM 2500 gas turbines; 80,000hp = 30kt.
Weapons:	*AAW*: 2 twin launchers Mk 26 for Standard SM-1 MR (24 + 44 missiles); 2 20mm Phalanx CIWS.
	ASuW: 2 quadruple launchers for Harpoon missiles; 2 5in (127mm, 2 × 1) Mk 45 DP.
	ASW: 1–2 SH-2F Seasprite helicopters; ASROC missiles from after Mk 26 launcher (see below); 2 triple Mk 32 tubes for Mk 46 torpedoes.
Sensors:	*Surveillance*: SPS-48A, SPS-55.
	Fire control: SPG-51 (2), SPG-60, SPQ-9A.
	Sonars: SQS-53A.
Complement:	348.

The four destroyers of the Kidd class were originally part of an order for six air defence (AAW) destroyers placed with the Ingalls Shipyard by Iran in 1974. The design was based on the Spruance, with a twin-arm Mk 26 launcher forward in place of the Mk 16 ASROC "pepperbox", and a second Mk 26 launcher aft in place of Sea Sparrow. The radar outfit was modified accordingly, with

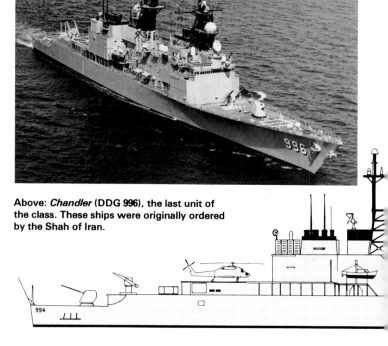

Above: *Chandler* (DDG 996), the last unit of
the class. These ships were originally ordered
by the Shah of Iran.

Above: *Scott* (DDG 995) shortly after completion. These ships are based on the Spruance design, but have an air defence mission. Mk 26 twin-arm launchers have replaced ASROC and Sea Sparrow.

an SPS-48 3-D set replacing the SPS-40 of *Spruance,* and SPG-51 tracker/illuminators forward and aft.

Two of the six units initially projected were cancelled by Iran before contracts were signed in March 1978. Orders for the first two ships were subsequently cancelled in early 1979 (when both had been laid down) by the new Islamic government of Ayatollah Khomeini, and the third and fourth hulls were cancelled shortly afterwards. The contracts were subsequently taken over at a bargain price by the US government, and all four ships were duly completed for the US Navy in 1981–82. The pennant numbers reflect their place in the Spruance production line, and do not fit in with the hull-numbering sequence for US Navy guided missile destroyers.

As designed, these ships had a number of features specifically requested by the Iranians, including dust filters for the air intakes and greater air-conditioning capacity. They failed to meet US Navy standards in a number of other respects; several modifications were made during construction, and additional weapons systems and electronics have been fitted since completion.

The magazine for the forward Mk 26 Mod 0 launcher has a capacity of 24 Standard SM-1 MR missiles, but the Mod 1 launcher aft has a larger magazine which holds 16 ASROC anti-submarine missile rounds as well as 28 Standards. The ships are unusual in the US Navy in having only one SPG-51 tracker/illuminator ▶

Below: *Callaghan* (DDG 994) as completed. The Vulcan/Phalanx 20mm CIWS guns are disposed *en echelon*, like the gas turbine uptakes. The forward mounting is to starboard, the after one to port.

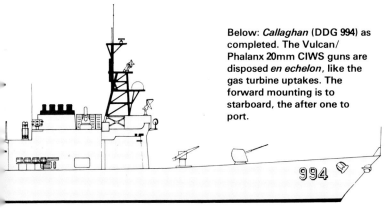

▶ per launcher, but the SPG-60 radar associated with the Mk 86 gun fire control system can also control the Standard missile, making three missile channels available.

Another unusual feature is the absence of a separate air surveillance radar, the SPS-48 being employed both for initial detection and for target designation to the SPG-51 tracker/illuminators. Quadruple Harpoon missile launchers have been added amidships since completion, and there are now Vulcan/Phalanx 20mm CIWS mountings atop the bridge structure to starboard and abreast the second funnel. SLQ-32(V)2 electronic countermeasures, Mk 36 Super RBOC chaff launchers and URN-25 TACAN are also being fitted to bring the ships in line with other contemporary US destroyers.

The ships were not originally intended to have any underwater detection system other than the SQS-53A bow-mounted sonar, but they are now scheduled to receive the SQR-19 TACTAS towed array during future overhauls. The additional weight of the new weapons systems, plus the fitting of Kevlar and aluminium alloy armour, has increased the full load displacement by about 1,000 tons over the original design.

Right: *Kidd* (DDG 993), the name-ship of the class. The pennant numbers of these ships do not fit in with the missile destroyer sequence, but follow on from the Spruance class.

Below: Another view of *Scott* (DDG 995). These ships are unusual in the US Navy in having no separate air surveillance radar. The large SPS-48 performs both the search and 3-D tracking functions.

Coontz class

Completed: 1959–61.
Names: DDG 37 *Farragut*; DDG 38 *Luce*; DDG 39 *MacDonough*; DDG 40 *Coontz*; DDG 41 *King*; DDG 42 *Mahan*; DDG 43 *Dahlgren*; DDG 44 *William V. Pratt*; DDG 45 *Dewey*; DDG 46 *Preble*.
Displacement: 4,700 tons standard; 5,950–6,150 tons full load.
Dimensions: Length 513ft (156.2m) oa; beam 53ft (16m); draught 25ft (7.6m).
Propulsion: 2-shaft geared steam turbines; 85,000hp = 34kt.
Weapons: *AAW*: 1 twin launcher Mk 10 for Standard SM-1 ER (40 missiles).
ASuW: 2 quadruple launchers for Harpoon missiles; 1 5in (127mm) Mk 42 DP.
ASW: 1 8-cell launcher Mk 16 for ASROC; 2 triple Mk 32 tubes for Mk 44/46 torpedoes.
Sensors: *Surveillance*: SPS-48, SPS-29 or SPS-49, SPS-10B.
Fire control: SPG-55B (2); SPG-53A.
Sonars: SQS-23 (SQQ-23 PAIR in DDG 37, 45).
Complement: 377.

Originally designated "frigates", like their immediate successors of the Leahy and Belknap classes, the ten ships of the Coontz class were reclassified as guided missile destroyers in 1975. They are the only US destroyers with the Standard Extended Range (ER) missile, the other frigate classes being reclassified as cruisers. The Standard SM-1 ER is a two-stage missile with a length of 26ft (7.9m) and a maximum range of 30–40nm (55–75km). Its size precludes vertical loading, and the missiles are housed in two horizontal magazine rings located within the hull; they are loaded at an angle on to the twin-arm Mk 10 launcher from a missile ready room immediately abaft the launcher. Standard employs semi-active guidance, and is controlled by two large SPG-55 tracker/illuminators.

Right: *Farragut* **(DDG 37), the only unit of the Coontz class to be fitted with a reload magazine for her Mk 16 ASROC launcher.**

Below: *Luce* **(DDG 38) underway. These ships are the only former US Navy "frigates" to be reclassified as destroyers.**

Above: *Mahan* (DDG 42) retains her SPS-29 air surveillance radar. All ships of this class now have quadrupled Harpoon launchers in place of the twin 3in guns with which they were originally completed.

► On the Coontz class the Standard missile installation occupies the after part of the ship. There is a single 5in Mk 42 gun mounting on the forecastle, and an eight-cell launcher for ASROC anti-submarine missiles above it. Triple Mk 32 torpedo tubes are fitted at 01 deck level abreast the bridge structure, and quadruple launchers for Harpoon anti-ship missiles have recently been installed abreast the after superstructure in place of the former twin 3in AA mountings.

The Coontz class were designed as carrier escorts, and have been constantly updated throughout their service careers. From 1970 to 1977 all underwent a major modernisation programme which involved the replacement of the original Terrier missile with Standard, the replacement of the original SPS-39 3-D target designation radar by the more powerful SPS-48 model, and the installation of a Naval Tactical Data System (NTDS), which enables them to exchange target data with other similarly-equipped units on a real-time basis, thereby ensuring a rapid and economical distribution of targets and maximising the overall effectiveness of the task force. DDG 37, the first ship to undergo modernisation, had an ASROC reload magazine installed at the base of the bridge structure and received a taller mainmast, but these features were not extended to the other units of the class because of weight and cost factors.

Some ships are now receiving the SQQ-23A PAIR sonar, which employs two separate domes, in place of the earlier SQS-23, but although DDG 41 conducted sea trials of the Vulcan/Phalanx 20mm CIWS in 1973–74, this weapon will not be fitted in the class because of age, space and weight considerations.

DDG-42 is currently serving as trials ship for the New Threat Upgrade (NTU) refit. Modifications include an SPS-48D 3-D radar, SPS-49(V)5 air surveillance radar, and the SYS-2 computerised action information system. These modifications have enabled the ship to fire the Standard SM-2 ER missile, which requires target illumination only in its terminal homing phase. Whereas only two SM-1 missiles could be controlled simultaneously, the SM-2 is capable of multi-target engagements, enabling the ship to keep several missiles in the air at the same time. Other units of the class could undergo NTU refits if it is decided to extend their service lives into the 1990s, but the class is one of those due for replacement by the Arleigh Burke type (qv), and the ships' advanced age may preclude any further modernisation.

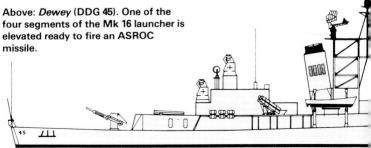

Above: *Dewey* **(DDG 45). One of the four segments of the Mk 16 launcher is elevated ready to fire an ASROC missile.**

Above: *Coontz* (DDG 40), the nameship of the class. These ships are the only US vessels in the destroyer category which can launch the extended range (ER) version of the Standard SM-1 missile. The magazine comprises two horizontal rings each of 20 missiles. Note the quadruple Harpoon canisters to port.

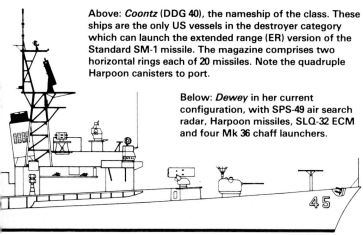

Below: *Dewey* in her current configuration, with SPS-49 air search radar, Harpoon missiles, SLQ-32 ECM and four Mk 36 chaff launchers.

Charles F. Adams class

Completed:	1960–64.
Names:	DDG 2 *Charles F. Adams*; DDG 3 *John King*; DDG 4 *Lawrence*; DDG 5 *Claude V. Ricketts*; DDG 6 *Barney*; DDG 7 *Henry B. Wilson*; DDG 8 *Lynde McCormick*; DDG 9 *Towers*; DDG 10 *Sampson*; DDG 11 *Sellers*; DDG 12 *Robison*; DDG 13 *Hoel*; DDG 14 *Buchanan*; DDG 15 *Berkeley*; DDG 16 *Joseph Strauss*; DDG 17 *Conyngham*; DDG 18 *Semmes*; DDG 19 *Tattnall*; DDG 20 *Goldsborough*; DDG 21 *Cochrane*; DDG 22 *Benjamin Stoddert*; DDG 23 *Richard E. Byrd*; DDG 24 *Waddell*.
Displacement:	3,570 tons standard; 4,825 tons full load.
Dimensions:	Length 437ft (133.2m) oa; beam 47ft (14.3m); draught 20ft (6.1m).
Propulsion:	2-shaft geared steam turbines; 70,000shp = 31.5kt.
Weapons:	*AAW*: 1 twin launcher Mk 11 for Standard SM-1 MR (42 missiles) in DDG 2–15; 1 single launcher Mk 13 (40 missiles) in DDG 16–24. *ASuW*: Harpoon missiles from Mk 11 or Mk 13 launchers; 2 5in (127mm, 2 × 1) Mk 42 DP. *ASW*: 1 8-cell launcher Mk 16 for ASROC; 2 triple Mk 32 tubes for Mk 44/46 torpedoes.
Sensors:	*Surveillance*: SPS-52B/C or SPS-39A, SPS-40B/D or SPS-37, SPS-10F. *Fire control*: SPG-51C (2); SPG-60, SPQ-9A in DDG 19, 20, 22; SPG-53A in others. *Sonars*: SQQ-23A PAIR (SQS-23D in DDG 19).
Complement:	339–354.

Above: *Towers* (DDG 9). The Charles F. Adams class has been one of the most successful postwar designs. Twenty-three units of the class were built for the US Navy, and a further six ships are in service with allied navies.

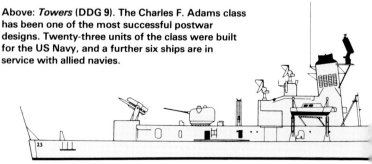

Above: *Sampson* (DDG 10), still in her original configuration except for the replacement of the SPS-39 3-D tracking radar by the planar SPS-39A. Many of the older ships of the class are now receiving the SPS-40 medium-range air search radar in place of the obsolescent SPS-37 (seen here atop the foremast).

The Charles F. Adams class is derived from the Forrest Sherman design, with a Tartar/Standard missile launcher in place of the third 5in gun mounting. It is still the standard air defence destroyer in service with the US Navy, and is employed together with the larger missile cruisers to provide protection for the carrier battle groups.

The first 14 ships of the class were fitted with the twin-arm Mk 11 launcher, but later ships have the single-arm Mk 13. The Mk 13 is a lightweight launcher with a high rate of fire — eight rounds per minute — which compensates in part for the single arm. Both launchers employ a cylindrical magazine containing two concentric rings of missiles. Overall length was increased by about 20ft (6m) over the ►

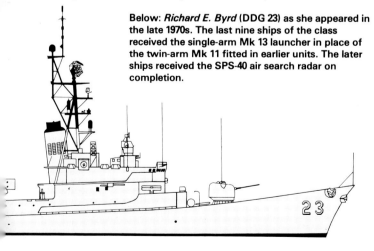

Below: *Richard E. Byrd* (DDG 23) as she appeared in the late 1970s. The last nine ships of the class received the single-arm Mk 13 launcher in place of the twin-arm Mk 11 fitted in earlier units. The later ships received the SPS-40 air search radar on completion.

Forrest Sherman in order to accommodate a Mk 16 ASROC launcher between the funnels. The installation of Tartar (since replaced by the Standard SM-1 MR missile) and ASROC made the Charles F. Adams one of the most formidably armed destroyers of its period, and the design was adopted by the Federal German and Australian Navies (qv).

In spite of their advanced age the ships are still highly regarded by the US Navy. In the late 1970s it was therefore proposed that they should undergo a major modernisation programme which would extend their service life beyond the nominal 30-year mark. Funding was to have been authorised in FY 1980–83, but financial considerations reduced the modernisation programme initially to ten, and subsequently to only three ships: DDG 19 emerged from refit in 1982, and DDG 20 and 22 followed in 1984 and 1985 respectively.

The modernisation has focused largely on electronics. The SPS-39 3-D radar has been replaced by an SPS-52C, and the SPS-40 air surveillance radar has been upgraded. The original gun fire control system has been replaced by the digital Mk 86, with SPG-60 and SPQ-9A radars, and an SYS-1 data system with UYA-4 NTDS has been provided. Installation of the SPG-60 radar makes a third

missile channel available for air defence engagements. Electronic counter-measures and communications have also been updated.

The remaining 20 ships are being upgraded during routine overhauls. SPS-40 and SPS-52B radars are replacing the original models, the ECM and communications outfits are being updated, and a digital computer system is being provided for the Mk 68 GFCS in some ships. The SQQ-23 PAIR active/passive sonar is replacing the original SQS-23.

All ships of the class have had their Mk 11 or Mk 13 launchers modified to fire the Harpoon anti-ship missile. Four Harpoons are generally carried by ships with the Mk 11 launcher, six by later units armed with the Mk 13.

The Charles F. Adams class is one of those scheduled for replacement by the Arleigh Burke class, and the unmodernised units of the class can expect to begin paying off towards the end of this decade, when the new hulls come on line.

Below: *Barney* (DDG 6), with the twin-arm Mk 11 launcher and her original radar outfit. Three ships of this class have recently been fitted with the Mk 86 digital GFCS in place of the elderly Mk 68.

Spruance class

Completed: 1975–83.

Names: DD 963 *Spruance*; DD 964 *Paul F. Foster*; DD 965 *Kinkaid*; DD 966 *Hewitt*; DD 967 *Elliott*; DD 968 *Arthur W. Radford*; DD 969 *Peterson*; DD 970 *Caron*; DD 971 *David W. Ray*; DD 972 *Oldendorf*; DD 973 *John Young*; DD 974 *Comte De Grasse*; DD 975 *O'Brien*; DD 976 *Merrill*; DD 977 *Briscoe*; DD 978 *Stump*; DD 979 *Conolly*; DD 980 *Moosbrugger*; DD 981 *John Hancock*; DD 982 *Nicholson*; DD 983 *John Rodgers*; DD 984 *Leftwich*; DD 985 *Cushing*; DD 986 *Harry W. Hill*; DD 987 *O'Bannon*; DD 988 *Thorn*; DD 989 *Deyo*; DD 990 *Ingersoll*; DD 991 *Fife*; DD 992 *Fletcher*; DD 997 *Hayler*.

Displacement: 5,920 tons light; 8,040 tons full load.

Dimensions: Length 563ft (171.7m) oa; beam 55ft (16.8m); draught 29ft (8.8m) max.

Propulsion: 2-shaft COGAG; 4 General Electric LM 2500 gas turbines; 80,000hp = 32kt.

Weapons: *AAW*: 1 8-cell launcher Mk 29 for Sea Sparrow (24 missiles); 2 20mm Phalanx CIWS.
ASuW: 2 quadruple launchers for Harpoon missiles; 2 5in (127mm, 2 × 1) Mk 45 DP.
ASW: 1–2 SH-2F Seasprite helicopters; 1 8-cell launcher Mk 16 for ASROC (24 reloads); 2 triple Mk 32 tubes for Mk 46 torpedoes.

Sensors: *Surveillance*: SPS-40/B/C/D (SPS-49 in DD 997), SPS-55.
Fire control: SPG-60, SPQ-9A, Mk 91.
Sonars: SQS-53A/B.

Complement: 250.   ▶

Above: *Spruance* (DD 963), the lead-ship of the class, as first completed. She lacks a number of major items of equipment; this only serves to emphasize the large block-like superstructures.

Below: A more recent view of *Spruance,* now fitted with Harpoon anti-ship missiles, SLQ-32 ECM equipment and NATO Sea Sparrow.

Above: *Caron* (DD 970), displaying one of her two newly installed Vulcan/Phalanx 20mm CIWS guns atop the bridge structure.

The most controversial ship-type to be built for the US Navy since World War II, the Spruance class was designed to replace the war-built destroyers of the Gearing and Allen M. Sumner classes. At 8,000 tons full load — more than twice the displacement of the destroyers it was to replace — the Spruance epitomised the US Navy's design philosophy of the 1970s. This philosophy envisaged the construction of large hulls with block superstructures which maximised internal volume, fitted out with machinery which could easily be maintained, and equipped with high-technology weapons systems which could be added to and updated by modular replacement at a later stage. The object was to minimise "platform" costs, which have no military pay-off, in favour of greater expenditure on weapons systems ("payload") to ensure that the ships would remain first-line units throughout the 30-year life expectancy of their hulls. In line with the principle of reducing "platform" costs to minimum, the entire class was ordered from a single shipbuilder, the Litton/Ingalls Corporation, which used advanced modular construction techniques at a purpose-built production facility at Pascagoula.

The controversy which surrounded the Spruance class when the first units entered service in the mid-1970s centred on the small number of visible weapons. The advanced ASW qualities of the design are, however, largely hidden within the hull and the bulky superstructures. The ASROC launcher has a magazine beneath it holding no fewer than 24 reloads. The large hangar to port of the after funnel measures 54ft by 23ft (16.5m × 7m) and can accommodate two LAMPS-I helicopters. The triple Mk 32 torpedo tubes, which are concealed behind sliding doors in the hull, are served by a central torpedo magazine containing 20 Mk 46 torpedoes. The SQS-53 low-frequency bow sonar, a solid-state version of the SQS-26, can operate in a variety of active and passive modes, including "direct path", "bottom bounce" and "convergence zone". It has proved so successful that the SQS-35 variable-depth sonar initially scheduled for installation in these ships will not now be fitted. ▶

Below: *Arthur W. Radford* (DD 968) as she appeared in the late 1970s, still lacking SLQ-32 ECM and Phalanx.

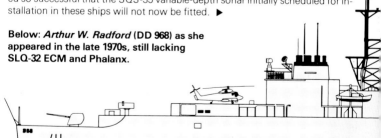

Above: *Fletcher* (DD 992), as yet without her Phalanx Close-In Weapon System fitted but with all other systems in place.

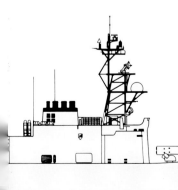

Above: *John Young* (DD 973), with her forward 5in Mk 45 trained to port. The Mk 16 ASROC launcher forward of the bridge has a magazine beneath it housing 24 reload missiles. Two LAMPS-I helicopters can be accommodated in the hangar.

▶ The adoption of an all-gas-turbine propulsion system, which employs paired LM 2500 turbines *en echelon* in a unit arrangement, and which was selected partly because of the ease with which it can be maintained and the consequent economics in engine-room personnel, has resulted in a significant reduction in underwater noise emission. Gas turbines are also used instead of the customary diesels to generate electrical power. The hull-form was designed to minimise rolling and pitching, enabling the ships to dispense with stabilisers, which are also a source of underwater noise.

The 5in Mk 45 gun is a lightweight model with modest performance in the anti-aircraft role but of greater reliability than the complex Mk 42 mounting fitted in earlier destroyers. It was originally envisaged that the forward Mk 45 mounting would be replaced by the 8in Mk 71 (203mm) Major Caliber Light Weight Gun (MCLWG) under development in the mid-1970s, but this project was subsequently cancelled. Early units of the class were completed without Harpoon or Sea Sparrow, but these have now been retrofitted, together with SLQ-32(V)2 ECM and Mk 36 Super RBOC chaff launchers. All ships are currently being fitted with two Phalanx 20mm CIWS and the Mk 23 Target Acquisition System (TAS), which uses a fast-rotating antenna mounted on the aft-facing platform of the mainmast to detect low-flying missiles. The ships are also being fitted with Kevlar plastic armour to protect their vital spaces.

Right: *Caron* as first completed, still lacking a number of items of equipment. These ships were initially criticised for being under-armed, but are now recognised to be very effective anti-submarine units. They have also received additional weapons systems since completion which enable them to defend themselves more effectively against air attack and to undertake independent surface operations. They would normally be employed as part of a carrier battle group, and would rely on other vessels to provide area air defence.

Left: *Briscoe* (DD 977), with SLQ-32 ECM abaft the fore-funnel. The uptakes for the gas turbine exhausts are offset to port and to star-board. These ships also employ gas turbines to generate their electrical power, and all machinery is flexibly mounted to reduce noise emission.

Numerous modifications are planned for the future. Nine ships (including DD 974, 976, 979, 981, 984, 985 and 989) are scheduled to receive eight Tomahawk missiles housed in two quadruple armoured box launchers during the mid-1980s. Other units (including DD 963, 964, 966, 990 and 991) will have their ASROC launcher and its magazine replaced by a 32-cell Mk 41 vertical launch module which will hold up to 29 Tomahawk and, later, vertical-launch ASROC missiles. As the Mk 41 VL module can also launch the Standard SM-2 area defence missile, there is a possibility that this could also be launched under the control of an accompanying Aegis-equipped ship of the Ticonderoga or Arleigh Burke class. It is planned to fit the SQR-19 TACTAS towed array in all ships at some future date, but its introduction has been delayed.

SInce 1981 *Merrill* has been serving as trials ship for the General Electric EX-83 CIWS system, which is based on the GAU-8 30mm Gatling gun; she was also scheduled to conduct trials of an extended-range version of Sea Sparrow. *Hayler* has a Mk 86 Mod. 10 gun fire control system, which enables her Mk 45 guns to fire semi-active laser-guided projectiles. This system offers considerable potential for the fire-support mission, and a production version may well be retrofitted to all ships of the class. The Spruance design has been used as the basis for the Kidd class destroyers (pages 134–137) and the Aegis cruisers of the Ticonderoga class.

OTHER SUPER-VALUE MILITARY GUIDES IN THIS SERIES......

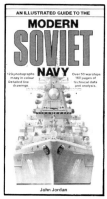

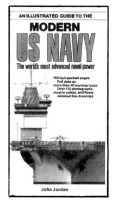

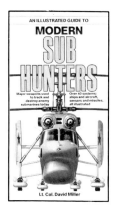

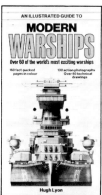

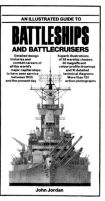

OTHER ILLUSTRATED MILITARY GUIDES NOW AVAILABLE

Air War over Vietnam
Allied Fighters of World War II
Bombers of World War II
Electronic Warfare
Elite Forces
Future Fighters
German, Italian and Japanese Fighters
   of World War II
Israeli Air Force
Military Helicopters
Modern Airborne Missiles
Modern American Fighters

Modern Fighters and Attack Aircraft
Modern Naval Aviation
Modern Soviet Air Force
Modern Soviet Ground Forces
Modern Tanks
Modern US Air Force
Modern US Army
NATO Fighters
Pistols and Revolvers
Rifles and Sub-Machine Guns
Spy Planes
World War II Tanks

* Each has 160 fact-filled pages
* Each is colourfully illustrated with hundreds of action photographs and technical drawings
* Each contains concisely presented data and accurate descriptions
   of major international weapons
* Each represents tremendous value

If you would like further information on any of our titles please write to:
Publicity Dept. (Military Div.), Salamander Books Ltd.,
52 Bedford Row, London WC1R 4LR

PRINTED IN BELGIUM BY
proost
INTERNATIONAL BOOK PRODUCTION